CW00547162

Bill 'Swampy' Marsh is an awarding-winning writer and performer of stories, songs and plays. He spent most of his youth in rural south-western New South Wales. Swampy was forced to give up any idea he had of a 'career' as a cricketer after a stint at agricultural college was curtailed because of illness, and so began his hobby of writing. After backpacking through three continents and working in the wine industry, his writing hobby blossomed into a career.

Swampy runs writing workshops throughout schools and communities, and is employed part-time through the Adelaide Institute of TAFE's professional writing unit. He has won and judged many nationwide short story writing competitions, and performs his stories and songs regularly on radio, television and stage. His plays have been performed across Australia.

To discover more about Swampy's work, visit www.billswampymarsh.com

Other books by this author

Beckom Pop. 64
Old Yanconian Daze
Looking For Dad
Great Australian Flying Doctor Stories
Great Australian Shearing Stories
Great Australian Droving Stories
More Great Australian Flying Doctor Stories

Great Australian
RAILWAY STORIES

Bill 'Swampy' Marsh

ABC
Books

Variations on 'The Train' and 'The War Hero' were written by Bill 'Swampy' Marsh and published by Hudson Publishing in Bill's first book titled, *Beckom Pop. 64*. The story 'The Train' received a commendation in the 1988 FAW Victorian Literary Awards.

 The ABC 'Wave' device is a trademark of the Australian Broadcasting Corporation and is used under licence by HarperCollins*Publishers* Australia.

First published in Australia in 2005
This edition published in 2008
by HarperCollins*Publishers* Australia Pty Limited
ABN 36 009 913 517
harpercollins.com.au

Copyright © Text: Bill Marsh 2005
Copyright © Photographs: resides with individual photographers

The right of Bill Marsh to be identified as the author of this work has been asserted by him in accordance with the *Copyright Amendment (Moral Rights) Act 2000*.

This work is copyright. Apart from any use as permitted under the *Copyright Act 1968*, no part may be reproduced, copied, scanned, stored in a retrieval system, recorded, or transmitted, in any form or by any means, without the prior written permission of the publisher.

HarperCollins*Publishers*
Level 13, 201 Elizabeth Street, Sydney NSW 2000, Australia
Unit D, 63 Apollo Drive, Rosedale, Auckland 0632, New Zealand
A 53, Sector 57, Noida, UP, India
1 London Bridge Street, London SE1 9GF, United Kingdom
2 Bloor Street East, 20th floor, Toronto, Ontario M4W 1A8, Canada
195 Broadway, New York NY 10007, USA

ISBN 978 0 7333 2378 2

Cover designed by Avril Makula
Typeset in 11.5/15pt Granjon by Kirby Jones
Printed and bound in Australia by Griffin Press,
70gsm Classic used by HarperCollins*Publishers* is a natural, recyclable product made from wood grown in sustainable forests. The manufacturing processes conform to the environmental regulations in the country of origin, Finland.

To my mother with love—Vicky Marsh—Gem of
the West, a ganger's daughter

Contents

Acknowledgements

In memory of Alan and Shirley Byrnes, Alf Harris,
Reg Hart, Danny Leoni, Errol McInnes and Joe
Rawson.

Special thanks for their research and support:
    Jeff Austin (Railway's Historian, Bayswater, WA)
    Ben Bennett (Mt Eliza, Victoria)
    Chris Carter (Adelaide, SA)
    Ron Carter (Sulphide Street Station Railway and
Historical Museum, Broken Hill, NSW)
    Tony Coen (Derwent Valley Railway Museum,
New Norfolk, Tasmania)
    Ron Fluck (National Railway Museum, Port
Adelaide, SA)
    Ted Gade (Port Augusta, SA)
    Nola and Mick Gallagher (Normanton, Queensland)
    David and Christine Harris (Mount Barker, SA)
    Ray Jaensch (Adelaide, SA)
    Margaret Loveday and Barbara Meredith
('Confused?' Business Solutions, Narrabeen, NSW)
    Peter Meale (Harry's Road House, Beckom, NSW)

David Mewes (Assistant Curator, The Workshops Rail Museum, North Ipswich, Queensland)

Laurie and Coral Nicholls (Andergrove, Queensland)

Shirley Norris (Griffith Pioneer Park Museum, Griffith, NSW)

Jim and Joy Oliver (Australian Railway Historical Society, Bassendene, WA)

Ron Potter (Railway Station Museum, Coolgardie, WA)

Mick Thomas and Gerry Galvan (Cootamundra, NSW)

Contributors

Great Australian Railway Stories is based on stories told to Bill 'Swampy' Marsh by:

Fred Abel
Megan Bajtek
Jack Bellinger
Norm Bewes
Owen Blackstock
Paul Brady
Colin Broad
Tom Bullen
Ron Carter
Tony Coen
Jack Connell
Ray Cook
Graham Cowell
Geoff Driver
Ted Gade
Brian Gibbs
Jack Goldsmith
Marion Harrington
Alf Harris
Reg Hart

Eddie Hastie
Elsie Jackson
Ray Jaensch
Bill Kelly
Stan Kingham
Allen Kleinig
Keith 'Bill' Langley
Steve Laub
Bill Legg
Jaan and Maree
    Lopsik
George McHugh
George McKay
Fred McKenzie
Vicky Marsh
Paul Mayhew
Claude Murta
Laurie and Coral
    Nicholls
David O'Connor

Jim and Joy Oliver
Len Opie
Norm Parry
Chris Parsons
Frank Partington
Norm Pearce
Jack Pitman
Roy Pool
Ron Potter
Betty Reynolds
Mavis St Clair
Bob Sloper
Ken Spinks
Nehama Stewart
Essie Syson
Trevor Tobin
Norm Wadeson
Geoff Walker

Foreword

By TIM FISCHER
Deputy Prime Minister of Australia (1996–1999)

Back in 1895, the celebrated American author Mark Twain came to Australia and caught a train or two, from Sydney to Melbourne to Castlemaine and beyond. During his visit he told some extraordinary tales as part of a lecture series to help raise funds to meet some business debts at home.

Subsequently, he wrote a famous book called *Tramps Abroad* which included many colourful tales about all that he endured with the break-of-gauge railway systems of Australia. His famous statement after changing trains at Albury reflected a good deal of colourful thinking when he wrote 'Now comes a singular thing, the oddest thing, the strangest thing, the unaccountable marvel that Australia can show, namely the break of gauge at Albury-Wodonga. Think of the paralysis of intellect that gave that idea birth.'

Eleven decades later another colourful author, namely Bill 'Swampy' Marsh, has come along to put down an authentic collection of great Australian railway yarns.

Many of the stories capture both the dedication and the determination of so many good railway people, often working in challenging conditions at remote locations all over Australia.

The culture attaching to the life and times of railway workers is almost tribal in nature, reflecting years of work practices and precedents, with a bonding and a trust at the grassroots level not always matched by the senior echelons of the various railway systems.

One of the biggest changes after the first one hundred years or so of operation was the progressive replacement of the giant steam engines with the faster and cleaner diesel-electric locomotives but, to the true afficionado, a far more sterile environment for operations ever since.

There is no doubt this one change of locomotive power completely altered the pattern of operations along all mainlines and branchlines, greatly reduced manning levels at many depots and, as a bonus, allowed for a big clean-up of major railway station buildings, such as Sydney Central station.

Some aspects of this arise in the many great stories Bill 'Swampy' Marsh has selected, polished up, and as a result created a collection of true yarns giving an insight into the culture of the railways of Australia over the years.

The nineteenth century saw the birth of rail in Great Britain and right around the world, the twentieth century saw the near death of rail due to the mass-produced motor car and mass-produced aircraft, the twenty-first century is seeing the revitalisation of rail worldwide. This is due to several factors including environmental and greenhouse factors, better operational policies, and at last some capital investments in rail infrastructure.

However, a common thread running through the railways is the human side, the great characters who overcame the hardship with a good sense of humour and made things happen.

Bill 'Swampy' Marsh demonstrates that this level of focus and commitment is as true today as it was back in 1831 when the first train ever ran in Australia, from just near the Newcastle Anglican Cathedral down across Hunter Street to the Coal Wharf, resulting in Australia's first exports of coal from Newcastle to the world, in this case to India.

James Steel was the first Chief Engineer of Australia's first railway, a private railway built and operated by the Australian Agricultural Company, and he was the man who decided that the first railway line should be built in the gauge his great friend and student colleague from the United Kingdom, George Stephenson, had created: 4' 8½".

From the life and times of James Steel in the early nineteenth century right through to today in the twenty-first century, many anecdotes have been created, many yarns have been spun, and now many stories recorded from the decades of operation of the various railways of Australia.

Introduction: The Train

When we first came up with the idea of my writing *Great Australian Railway Stories*, I was once again at a loss as to where to find the vast and varied number of people I needed to interview to fill the book with stories. As great an adventure as it would've been, ABC Books haven't the money to send a writer like me wandering all over Australia, chatting to people. If only. So I needed a way of getting out there, virtually, from my home base. To that end I wrote a letter to many of the contributors to my other books (*Great Flying Doctor Stories, Great Australian Shearing Stories* and *Great Australian Droving Stories*) asking them if they knew of anyone who might have a railway story to tell. I was overwhelmed with the response. What's more, even if some of these people didn't have a story to tell, they took the time and effort to seek out others who may have.

So *Great Australian Railway Stories* grew from the efforts of those many people who, like myself, are keen to capture tales of our past before they disappear. I'd like very much to mention a few of my previous contributors and supporters who have since died: my dear old friends Alan and Shirley Byrnes, who passed away within a month of each other and whose home was always open to me on my many travels, not only when on writing journeys, but in life itself; Danny Leoni, a great friend and mentor; Errol McInnes and my cousin, Joe Rawson, who were both a great help with the shearing stories. I'd also like to mention two great storytellers: Reg Hart, who had a couple of stories in the droving book and one in this book ('Jinks') and also Alf Harris who has two stories in this book ('Dennis the Menace' and 'Santa'). I mention their story titles for two reasons: first, when you read them you'll get some idea as to the gentlemanly character of these two men and, second, they both got to read their stories before they died and were very proud of the manner in which I wrote them—something that meant the world to me.

Also, in many ways, this book is a family effort. It's dedicated to my Mum—a ganger's daughter—who has a couple of her own memories included and who, at present, is a 'healthy' ninety-one years of age and we're hoping for more enjoyable years ahead; also to my sister Margaret who almost typed her fingers down to the knuckles while transcribing the taped interviews; my sister Barbara who, no doubt, being the elder of the two, kept a keen, managerial eye on things; to my partner, Margaret Worth, who continues to inspire me; and to my musical mate David Hansford, who proved that his expertise lay not only in his ability to make the songs I write sound half-listenable but took time out of the chaos of his own life to come to my aid when my computer crashed, the locks on my house doors seized, the hole in the kitchen wall needed painting, the plumbing went up the creek, the electricity down the spout etc.

As for my connection with railways, I reckon that if you've never smelt coal smoke from a steam train or got a cinder or three in your eye, then you've missed out on a lot. Other than my mum being a ganger's daughter, Central railway station has played a pivotal part in my life. As a kid, my mum and dad would take me down to Central, put a name tag around my neck and send me off up north to Broadmeadow (in Newcastle), where I'd meet my uncles and aunties for holidays. Those train journeys were such an exciting adventure that I never even gave it a thought that Mum and Dad might've just wanted me out of their hair for a couple of weeks. I still recall the train winding along the beautiful Hawkesbury River and stopping at little places like Woy Woy and Wyong, where spruikers paraded up and down the platform shouting, 'Oysters. Oysters.' And they'd come plump and fresh in those long skinny bottles.

When we moved out to the south-west of New South Wales and then, later on, when Mum and Dad went to live up the far north coast, Central railway station became a place where I'd sit for hours, waiting for some bush connection or other, being mesmerised by the blinking of the Penfolds purple neon grapes. There were trips to Cairns. Under the clock at Central was where I'd meet my girlfriend during my college days.

After returning from a two-year trip overseas Shirley and I travelled on the Indian Pacific from Perth, across the Nullarbor, where just outside the window lay so many of the answers to the questions I'd spent the previous couple of years wandering around the world trying to sort out. And finally, a memorable road trip up the old Ghan railway track to Alice Springs, where Dave and I performed at the Transport Hall of Fame Gala Dinner, on the same bill with Slim Dusty—the thrill of a lifetime.

I could go on but I'd just like to finish off my introduction with one of my favourite stories from my first book, *Beckom Pop. 64*, called 'The Train'.

I don't know exactly how old I was when it happened, but it was at primary school. And I recall our teacher standing in front of our class of five kids and announcing the news that, 'Throughout the history of the modern world, the train has played an important part as a purveyor of free trade'. And that's when Brownie, McCaughney and me came up with the idea.

See, we'd noticed that by the time the Temora Mail reached our remote little settlement of Beckom Pop. 64, the passengers were slumped into a deep, sedentary, mental state and it was while they were in this vulnerable condition that we felt they'd more than likely be prepared to buy anything. This, we hoped, included our abundance of figs.

Just once a week that old passenger train huffed, puffed, clattered and rocked its way slowly into Beckom railway station, there to rest its tired parts for a while and take on much-needed water and coal. So it was during this respite that Brownie, McCaughney and me decided to open up trade links with the outside world. We calculated that from the first sight of smoke on the horizon to the South West Mail's arrival at the station took about twenty to thirty minutes, depending upon the wind. And that'd give us enough time to pick a few buckets of figs and set up our little stall opposite where the passenger carriages stopped. We even painted a sign to announce our intentions. It read:

FRESH FIGS
1 PENNY A DOZEN

Now, old Tom, the widowed stationmaster, was all for it. He reckoned that our enterprise would not only help brighten up his week but our noisy arrival would also remind him that it was train day, an occasion he was apt to forget from time to time.

Anyhow, that first week of trade, all the figs sold immediately. You could see the keenness in the eyes of those weary travellers as they willingly exchanged their money for our produce. So relieved were these people from distant parts to look at a different human face for their brief time of stopover that, even after all the figs had been sold, they still crowded around us. They touched us to see if we were real and they tried to engage us in deep conversation by asking us questions like, 'What are your names?' and 'What class are you in at school?' Some even questioned us as to, 'What the bloody hell do you do for entertainment in a place like this?'

By the next week, when that old steam train had ground to a halt in our carefully set trade trap, we'd boosted the price of the figs up to threepence per dozen. And even though there were a few muffled complaints about both the price and the quality of our produce, the lot again sold effortlessly.

Fig season soon came to its mushy end but in its place came oranges and almost fresh ginger beer. Again, all stocks were snapped up eagerly, even at hugely inflated prices.

They say that success breeds success. And that's true because before long I was giving a well-received, and paid for, rendition of 'You Are My Sunshine' with old Tom playing the gum leaf, while Brownie wrestled with three tennis balls in an act he described as 'juggling'. Then McCaughney's broken leg proved to be such a great attraction that long after it'd mended he still wore the plaster cast. Oh, how those poor, travel-bored souls almost tripped over themselves just to pay for the privilege of signing their names on that dirty, scrappy, bit of plaster. And McCaughney's rendition of how the accident occurred was told so differently and graphically to each train load of people that, before long, we'd all forgotten how the leg was originally broken.

But the money kept pouring in.

Then one week the strangest thing happened. It was a still day and no smoke appeared on the horizon. Brownie jumped off the platform, put his ear to the railway track and reported that a train was definitely on its way. This we found hard to believe so we hopped down to join him and, yes, sure enough, an approaching train could be heard along the rails.

Then, echoing in the distance, there came a whistle. But somehow this whistle sounded different from the one we were used to hearing. This was more a sound of warning than of welcome. Together, we all stood at the platform's edge, gawking out along the track. Then, from out of the shimmering mirage appeared a monster the like of which we'd never seen before. We scampered back behind our small stall and huddled there for safety as this metal monstrosity roared down upon us with all the fury of a wild storm. It completely ignored Beckom and thundered by as if we never even existed. It left us quaking in our shorts and sandals.

In search of answers we looked at old Tom. 'Oh, that's one of them new diesel locomotives,' he said. 'They don't need no water or coal so there's no reason for 'em to stop in a small little town like this.' And I'm sure that I saw the tears welling in his eyes.

Turning back we witnessed the captured train carriages being dragged off, rudely, into the distance by this new diesel locomotive. Then we packed up our unsold produce and we walked home in stunned silence, amazed at just how viciously technology had severed our trading ties with the outside world.

A Child's Dream

Back in the early 1940s, when I was about six or seven, I clearly remember the time I was messing around in the bed of the Bremer River, in front of our house at Callington, just south-east of Adelaide. Anyway, Mr Paech, a local farmer, was bucketing water from a small pool into a tank on the back of his old buckboard, to take out for his sheep and horses to drink. And as kids used to do, I wandered across and started talking to Mr Paech and, after a while, he asked the time-honoured question, 'Now, Raymond,' he said, 'what're you going to do when you grow up?'

And, without a blink of the eye, I replied, 'Oh, I'm gonna be an engine driver, Mr Paech. I'm gonna drive steam trains.'

'Well, that's good, my boy,' he said. 'I hope you'll remember to give me a wave when you go past my place.'

'Oh no, Mr Paech,' I exclaimed, 'I won't be able to wave to you 'cos you'll be well dead by then.'

Of course, that remark was made with all the childhood innocence in the world so I couldn't understand why he gave such a hearty laugh. Yet, it certainly illustrates how, from my very earliest years, trains fascinated me so much that, come hell or high water, I was going to drive them when I grew up.

Anyhow, I went on to join the SAR (South Australian Railways) as a youth porter at Callington. That was on 8 December 1952, and twice weekly I was also required to work as assistant to the guard on the Sedan track. So, each Monday and Thursday morning a little RX-class steam loco left Mile End, with a brake van and a wagon or two in tow, and began its journey. The train stopped at Callington, usually between 12 noon and 1.00 pm, where I'd clamber aboard the brake van with my steel tucker box draped from my shoulder by a leather strap and off we'd chuff, down through the Bremer River Valley then up, over Callington Hill, and on to Monarto South.

At Monarto South we'd attach the loading that the big locos had previously hauled through the hills and left for our smaller loco to take on the Sedan line. We usually departed Monarto South between 1.00 and 2.00 pm and headed out over the old Princes Highway, northward to Pallanana, Tepko, Apamurra, Milendella, Sanderston, Kanappa, Cambrai and Sedan.

Now, depending on the amount of work to be done at each siding, we could reach Cambrai anywhere between 4.30 and 6.00 pm. On arrival we had goods to unload from the 'take-outs' wagon and usually there were empty wagons to be detached for the local grain agent. However, there were days when a far more important function had to be executed: it was payday for the local per-way gang and, yes, we were the paymasters, too. So, on a designated day each fortnight our brake van would contain a steel safe, and within the safe there'd be a large brown 'value' envelope, sealed with special sealing wax, addressed to 'The Ganger, Cambrai'.

The ganger at Cambrai was Andy Grieg, and Andy would sign for the 'value' before the fettlers arrived to collect their pay. There may well have been others including bridge painting gangs and carpenters but, even though it was nearly fifty years ago, I can still recall some of the characters. Rudi Pohl would roll up in a little baby Austin with several kids peering excitedly out the windows. Also there for their 'pound of flesh' was Charlie Fladrich, Charlie Hodges and Norm Fiegert.

After paying the gang we usually carried out the shunting and did the 'take-outs' and, more often than not, the driver, fireman and guard decided that some liquid refreshment was required before proceeding on to Sedan. Now, in those days, I was only aged about sixteen which was well below the drinking age of twenty-one years, so I'd be left stranded … but, on occasions, for good reason.

Incidentally, I must make it clear that these train crews were all a fine bunch. Sure, there were a few larrikins and characters amongst them, but that's usual. Anyhow, sometimes the crew told me that they were just going to nick over to the pub for a 'quickie' where, on the rare occasion, they'd inadvertently lose track of time. One time they were away for so long that the fire almost went out on the loco and we couldn't even raise enough steam to blow the whistle. Of course, that was a real one-off. But just how long the boys stayed over in the pub seemed to depend on three important factors: one was the intensity of the heat of the day; two was the magnitude of their thirst; and three was the amount of ready cash they had in their pockets.

Also remember, back then, we had six o'clock closing and to drink after that time one had to be, what was called, a 'bona-fide traveller'. At times I'd hear the train crew joking about signing the 'Bona-fide Traveller's Book' at the pub with names such as Donald Duck, Mickey Mouse, Brer Rabbit.

In retrospect it amazed me how no-one in Cambrai ever got on the blower and informed the rail authorities. You know, something like, 'Hey, do yer know what's goin' on up 'ere with some'a yer crews?' But no-one ever squealed. No-one ratted. No-one blew the whistle—perhaps it was because they, too, didn't have enough steam.

Now, the boys were always very generous of their time with me and they showed me the engine's workings, how to shunt, the whistle calling codes and so forth. But that's because they had an ulterior motive. See, on the occasion when it was as hot as hell, they were as thirsty as hell and if they had cash to burn they'd invite me to do the shunting while they were over in the pub. And that's when the opportunity to fulfil my most treasured childhood dream arose. Oh, I was in my element—my glory.

So, off they'd go, across the station yard, through the boundary fence and across the 'prairie' making a beeline for the pub. Great. I'd uncouple the train behind the last wagon to be shunted off at Cambrai before making my way forward to board the little RX loco. After clambering up the steel steps and into the cabin, I'd take up the driver's seat and release the air brakes. Slowly, I'd open the regulator—the throttle—to allow steam to rush into the cylinders and, with a loud hiss of steam, the loco would 'chuff, chuff, chuff' out along the main line with the wagons trailing behind. As I approached the Black Hill Road level crossing, I'd sound the designated whistle blast—a long, a short and a long—to warn of my train's approach.

Over the level crossing I'd continue on to a point where the last wagon had cleared the switches and I'd apply the brakes to stop the train. Down from the cabin I'd climb to run back and unlock the padlock on the 'cheese knob'—the device that sets the switches for the siding. Back to the loco I'd dash and take up my position in the driver's seat before winding the 'reversing wheel' into position. The air brakes were again released and another loud whistle blast before I opened the regulator and 'chuff, chuff, chuff', off I went in reverse, back into the freight siding.

At a point where I considered that the door of the 'take-out' wagon was adjacent to the door of the goods shed, I'd stop the train and run back and unload goods for Mr Schiller's shop, along with any other local goods. With the take-outs done, I'd push back to where Ron

Atkinson's grain stacks were situated and detach the empty wagons, there to await the loading of grain.

Everything was now in order. It was just a matter of putting the train back together. So, back into the driver's seat, the reversing wheel was wound to enable forward movement, the air brakes were released and the regulator was opened—'chuff, chuff, chuff', back out of the freight siding and onto the main line, then more whistle blasts for the Black Hill Road level crossing. The loco, with the take-out wagon attached, was then reversed back onto the remainder of the train and I'd couple up.

Mission accomplished. Now we were all set for the last leg of the journey, to Sedan. There was only one problem—no crew. They were still over at the pub. But they wouldn't be too long now, surely, then we'd go like hell to Sedan.

And so I'd wait for their arrival, satisfied that my childhood dream had come true. What's more, maybe I was even the youngest train driver in the world. Who knows? Still and all, I'd never be able to lay claim to that fame because, if the authorities ever found out, too many people would've gotten the sack, me included.

Anyway, dreams are quite personal things, aren't they?

Aladdin's Lamp

Railways run in the Nicholls family. My grandfather was a train driver at Kalgoorlie. It might sound a bit odd, but even though he was stationed in Western Australia he was employed by SAR (South Australian Railways). Then my father was a cook with the Commonwealth Railways; my uncle was a fireman with them as well. But I was a cleaner at Oodnadatta first, then one day the fireman on the Ghan took crook so they grabbed me to do the firing back to Quorn, and that's how I became a fireman. Then I went on to be a driver.

In those days the old Ghan line went from Port Augusta through Quorn, Hawker, Copley, Marree, Coward Springs, William Creek, Oodnadatta, Eringa, then up into the Northern Territory through Fink, Ewaninga and on to Alice Springs. See, a lot of people have the idea that only one Ghan train worked the line but there were heaps of others. Other than the passenger train there were stock trains, goods trains—you name it—work trains, coal trains, the lot.

Now as far as dates go, let me think; I left the Commonwealth Railways not long after I got married in 1950. Yes, that's right, because I met my wife, Coral Brooks, in Quorn, in '48. So I joined SAR in 1951, then I became a fireman, then a driver in 1953, and then that became AN (Australian National). But to be a driver on the Ghan in the old days was a real bloody honour, you know, because it was only the senior men, like the firemen, the guards and drivers, that ever worked the line.

But there were some characters, I can tell you. We had one guard by the name of Pud and, gawd, he'd pinch the milk out of your bloody coffee. You can't mention this, of course, but when we were working the cattle trains, if any of the cows calved along the way, to save them being trodden on and die, Pud'd take them down to the compo-brake van and put them in the bloody shower recess. The shower recess was the only place you could keep them, otherwise they'd shit everywhere. So there they'd be, all these bloody newborn calves in the brake van going, 'Moo, moo, moo', all bloody night.

Then when we got home, Pud'd take all these calves out to his place and, over time, he ended up with this bloody great big herd of cows. Oh, he had Herefords, he had Black Polls. He had bloody everything, which, of course, he then sold at a 100 per cent profit.

Then there's another story about Pud, which I also shouldn't mention. It was during the war and he was on a supply train going to the Alice and there was all this timber on a flat top. Well, Pud's got his eye on this timber, see, because he knows that he's got a few jobs back home that it could be used for. Anyhow, Pud knows that there's going to be a change of crew at Peak Creek; just before you get to Algebuckina. So the train stops there in the middle of the bloody night in amongst all these sandhills and Pud's up on the bloody flat-top sliding along this timber with the aim of hiding it in the sandhills and picking it up on his return journey. Anyhow, he's moving all this timber about and a bloody torchlight hits his eyes. It was the provos, the military police.

'What do you think you're doing?' one of the provos said.

'Thank Christ yer came along,' Pud replied. 'Some'a the bloody timber's coming off and I need a hand to get it back up on the flat-top.'

I mean, how's that for presence of mind, eh? But that was Pud. He was a nice guy but, as I said, give him half a chance and he'd nick the milk out of your coffee.

Then there's another favourite story of mine about a different bloke, a bloke called Bonny Fry. Bonny was the train examiner in Alice Springs. Geez, wasn't he a rough diamond. As a train examiner, it was Bonny's job to go along and check the brakes and everything on the Ghan before it departed the Alice. Now, I'd just finished shunting and I was going back to rest-out and, on that particular Monday, the Ghan was late leaving. Anyhow, I hooked up with Bonny and we were having a chat while he was doing this testing, and we came across this sleeping car.

Well, back in those days they had, like, the long-drop toilets on the trains. There wasn't even a pan or anything, so your business just went straight down onto the track. Inside the carriages they had all these signs telling everybody not to use the toilets while the train was standing at the station. Anyway, Bonny and me were going along beside this sleeping car and we hear this 'plop, plop' on the ground, and we see this stuff coming out the bloody chute.

'Gawd,' said Bonny, 'I've gotta clean this bloody mess up after they go.'

Now, Bonny had what was called a slush light. If you can imagine, a slush light's an oil can with a bloody big wick on it. To give you some idea, it's shaped exactly like a huge Aladdin's lamp. It was a hell of a size. Anyhow, he lights this Aladdin's lamp-looking thing, and he shoves it straight up the flue. Next thing, the window flies open but, instead of a beautiful genie appearing to grant us three wishes, this old dowager sticks her head out and, boy, didn't she start abusing poor old Bonny. Gawd, she was as mad as hell.

'Well, lady,' he said, 'if yer wanta have a shit here, then have it in the bloody station toilets where you're supposed to have it.'

But, geez, that lamp had a hell of a flame on it. I reckon it must've burnt every hair on her bum, and more besides.

All for Me Grog

I was eighteen when I joined the army, back in July 1942. Then, after our initial training was completed at Woodside Army Barracks, the orders came through from higher up in the chain that we were to be transferred to Canungra, south of Brisbane, before heading up to Ravenshoe, on the tablelands of north-eastern Queensland.

To that end we packed up all our gear and forwarded it on before catching the train over to the Melbourne suburb of Watsonia. All went exactly to plan so, when we arrived, we marched straight over to the railway station, ready and eager to board the train north. But, typical army fashion, there'd been some sort of mix-up from higher up in the chain of command and we'd arrived twenty-four hours early. So, with our gear heading north and us with nowhere else to go, we turned around and marched back to Watsonia, to spent the night without any clothing or anything.

The trip up north proved to be a real experience, especially with all the changes of rail gauge. What a mess that was. Typical state government parochialism—something they could never sort out. Every time we came to a state border, not only us passengers but, also, all the freight had to be transferred. So, trucks, tanks, vehicles, everything had to be lifted off one train and placed onto another, and it was all done by a combination of rudimentary equipment and bare hands.

Still, eventually we got to the Brisbane suburb of Indooroopilly, which was our last stop before we moved down to Canungra. There again, typical army, there'd been some sort of mix-up by those higher up in the chain and we'd been expected for breakfast at 5 am, but we arrived at 9 am, causing our much-awaited feast of bacon and eggs to be cold and congealed.

Then after our stint at Canungra we stayed overnight at the Exhibition Grounds, in Brisbane, before heading up to the Tablelands. At that stage we thought we were going to Burma, but that never eventuated. Perhaps there'd been another mix-up. But we did head north and it was while we were passing through Townsville that we came across a southbound freight train that happened to be carrying grog. Of course, with typical Australian ingenuity, somebody nabbed an eight-gallon keg of beer. The only trouble was, the provos—the military police—somehow got wind that there was this keg of beer on our train. Anyhow, the provos pulled up our train and they decided to search for this keg. Of course, being wartime, both the army and the railways had a strict timetable to keep—as I said, everything had to run like clockwork—so, after the provos had boarded the train, they told the driver to continue on the journey.

Now, in the Australian army, it was a matter of principle that the provos were to be 'cordially' hated. That was without question. They also had this reputation of not being a particularly bright mob. And it was this perceived lack of brightness that was just what we needed, because the provos decided to begin their search at the front of the train and systematically work their way through the eight or so carriages until they got to the back. Now, being Australians, it was out of the question that we'd ditch the keg while there was any grog remaining. So our only chance was to set up the keg in the last dogbox—compartment—in the last carriage then stall the progress of the provos while we got to it and knocked off the beer. Everybody was in on it. All for one, one for all, and all for me grog.

As far as the stalling procedure went, the first delaying point—or blockage point, as I'll call it—was that there were eight of us packed into each dogbox with all our gear and still the provos insisted on looking everywhere, even under the seats, which were not even high enough to conceal a keg. Also in our favour was, with the Queensland trains running on narrow gauge track, the carriages only had a narrow corridor and that also proved to be an ideal blockage point. The other blockage point was the toilets. The provos insisted on searching the toilets. So, suddenly, all the toilets were filled with personnel and, when the provos came knocking, they were greeted with a painfully muffled reply from within explaining how it was impossible for the occupant to vacate the unit because he was suffering from every diarrhoea-causing ailment known and unknown to mankind.

Anyhow, while the provos doggedly worked their way back to the end of the train we relaxed and worked our way through this keg of beer. And a nice drop it was, too. And it was with almost a military precision that those higher up in the chain couldn't seem to manage that we'd just finished the keg and had tossed it off the back of the train when, who should arrive: the provos.

And Still

Well, I'm a steam buff so railways and their history have always been a favourite subject of mine. That's why I'm sorry to see the demise of our steam locos and the closure of so many railway lines, Australia-wide. However, that said, my railway story isn't about a train as such but it does involve circumstances leading to a ride along a railway line.

It was 1956, the year of the big flood. The Murrumbidgee River was running a banker. Water covered the Lobidgee flood plain. The Sturt Highway was cut between Hay and Balranald, as well as in many other places. The road from our property, out to the highway, was inundated with so much water that car travel was impossible. So we were virtually living on an island and the only way we could get to Balranald was by flat bottom boat, part of the way, then to walk through mud and slush and more water until we reached the highway. So, to say the least, the situation was desperate, and still the rain continued to tumble down and the waters continued to rise.

Anyhow, our neighbour had a bulldozer and that's what we relied upon to maintain the levee banks around the house. Some of the sheds were already standing in water. But then the bulldozer broke down. Now, luckily the phones were still working so we got in touch with the caterpillar agency and, after explaining the dire urgency of our situation, the agent said he'd send out a serviceman. Of course, as I'd mentioned, the serviceman could only get out so far by car, then he had to slog it through some terrible conditions, before we could bring him the last distance out to our remote little island by boat.

So that's what he did and, after many hours of working out in the downpour, this serviceman finally stripped the bulldozer down. After having a look at the assembled bits and pieces, he scratched his head and announced that the crankshaft was knackered and it had to be re-ground before he could repair the bulldozer. And still the rain continued to tumble down and the waters continued to rise.

I forget why now but, for some reason, we couldn't take the crankshaft in the boat nor his car. So, it was shanks's pony all the way or, in other words, we had to walk. Now, have you ever seen a crankshaft out of a bulldozer? Well, it's all bends and bumps and bits and pieces. So to carry one is no easy task, as I was soon to find out, because it was me who somehow stuck up my hand and volunteered to help the serviceman carry the thing back to Balranald.

Now, as for the distance we had to cover; first, it was 13 miles out to the Sturt Highway then a further 7 miles into town. Anyhow, off we headed carrying this crankshaft. To start with, we walked for a couple of miles through ankle-deep water, mud and slush, while falling into an occasional deep hole to keep us on guard. Then we hit non-flooded ground for a couple of miles before we began wading through water of varying depths. Sometimes it was ankle deep, then suddenly you'd find yourself cock deep and struggling. Of course, the crankshaft was forever being dropped, dragged and bumped along the way. And still, the rain continued to tumble down and the waters continued to rise.

Still and all, we eventually staggered out over the railway line, much the worse for wear, and onto the relative dry of the Sturt Highway. Then we set off towards Balranald, hoping to catch a lift from a passing ute or truck, which wasn't very likely, considering our predicament and the atrocious conditions. Though, surprise, surprise, a ute soon appeared and we flagged it down. But as soon as the vehicle stopped, we knew it was a mistake. It was full of shearers who were as drunk as skunks, every one of them.

'Can yer give us a lift?' we asked.

'Bugger off,' they replied. 'Look at yerselves. Yer a bloody mess.'

Well, that was a complete kick in the bum considering the mess that these shearers were in. Anyhow, they took off down the road, leaving us standing there with the crankshaft. So the situation wasn't looking good. And still, the rain continued to tumble down and the waters continued to rise.

Then, as we were staggering along, wrestling with the crankshaft, there came a sound like a motorbike in the far distance. Of course, that didn't lift our hopes at all because, well, how could someone on a motorbike give a lift to two bedraggled blokes and a buggered bulldozer crankshaft.

But to our surprise, what had sounded like a motorbike came into view as a railway maintenance trike, coming down the line from Moulamein. Anyhow, we gave it one last effort and we stumbled over the distance to the track, where we flagged down the trike. And they stopped.

'Yeah,' the fettlers said. 'We'll take yers into town.'

So the railways came to our rescue and the maintenance trike saved the day. And still, the rain continued to tumble down and the waters continued to rise.

As Mad As

When I was about seventeen years old I started on the railways in Junee, working as a casual, shovelling coal. That was in 1939 and, in them days, when you shovelled down or level you got 11 pence ha'penny a ton but, when you threw it over your shoulder, it was a shilling a ton. Then I got on as a casual cleaner, cleaning the train engines, and eventually as cleaner. Oh, and I also done the call boy job around the town because I knew everybody. Calling was waking the drivers, the firemen and the guards up at whatever time of the day or night they wanted, to tell them what job they were doing. Some asked for half-an-hour's notice, others wanted an hour. It depended.

And in them days, God, in Junee alone there'd be dozens of call boys. See, there was four ordinary express trains of a night. Holiday time there'd be anything up to six or eight heading south to Albury and north to Sydney, then there'd be trains coming down from Narrandera and them places, out that way. So you might have to call forty to fifty men of a night. And well, the fireman, he could be living up one end of the bloody town and the driver might be up the other end. So you'd be going as flat as a tack from the time you got on the pushbike at eleven o'clock at night till your last call, say, around five or six in the morning. And there were some cranky blokes and there was some good blokes—same as usual.

But with the calling we had a lot of them cat's eyes. You know, the bindy, those prickle things with three sharp prongs. And they were bad. The bastards would puncture our tyres before we'd even gone 10 yards, if you gave them the chance. But we used to get a quarter of a cup of sugar and mix it to a paste with water then we'd suck it up into our bike pump and blow it into the tyres—just like the stuff they've got today for mending punctures—and that's what kept us out on the road.

Then, after Junee, I got on as a fireman and I went everywhere. But geez, some of them fellers used to drink, them days. Bloody hell, I remember one time carrying a drunk driver on me back from the Wagga railway station down to our loco with his false teeth clattering around in me pocket. Oh, I had to do the lot, then. I got the engine ready and I got the train out on the road—the track—while the driver just went to sleep on the floor with the diddy-box under his head. The diddy-box is the box with the detonators in it, in case you break down. So it would've given him one hell of a headache if the diddy-box had've blown up, eh.

Then another time with the drinking: see, there was a depot at Harden, a big barracks where all the fellers stayed over between trains, and it was a regular thing that, when you got to the barracks, you went down the pub for a few beers. Well, this particular night this train driver and his fireman, they had more than a few beers. They got stonkered, and around midnight they were on their way back to the barracks when they came across this rooster sitting on the fence.

'I'm feelin' hungry,' the driver said.

'Me too,' said the fireman.

So they got this bloody rooster by the scruff of the neck and they ringed it and they took him back to the railway barracks and they plucked him. And in the barracks, them days, they had those big coal ranges, so they stuck this rooster in a pot with some water and a bit of salt and pepper and they stuck it on this stove. Then, after an hour or so they opened up the tap at the bottom of the pot and they poured themselves a bit of soup and they reckon it was pretty good. Then an hour or so after that, into the barracks came a set of men from down the pub and the drunk fellers said, 'There's some soup in the pot there, have some.'

So these fellers go over and they fill up their mugs. Anyhow, after there's been about ten or so blokes had a go at this soup, these two blokes from Goulburn come in from off the job and they got a mugful and they're sitting by the stove drinking it and one of the drunk blokes said, 'How do yer reckon the soup's goin'?'

And the feller from Goulburn, he said, 'It's pretty good, only the barley could'a been cooked a bit longer.'

Then the drunk feller said, 'But we didn't put any barley in it.'

And another feller asked, 'Did you gut the fowl?'

'No,' they said, 'we didn't know nothin' about that. We just stuck the whole bloody lot in the pot.'

So they'd been eating all the guts and the giblets and every bloody thing. So they must've been pretty drunk, eh.

Then there was a feller by the name of Drew. He wasn't drunk; this's just another story. Anyhow, Drewie used to drive the train from Macksville to Coffs Harbour, taking kids to school. Well, one time he got to the railway barracks at Coffs Harbour and he was having a cup of tea there and the cleaning lady come over and she said, 'Geez, Mr Drew, I'm havin' trouble with the cockroaches.'

'I'll tell yer what to do,' Drewie said. 'Make up a mix of sulphur and lard and when yer catch a cockroach, roll him on his back and gently rub it onto his belly. Sure as eggs, it'll kill him.'

Then the cleaning lady, she said, 'Geez, Mr Drew, wouldn't it be simpler to just squash 'em with yer foot?'

And Drewie had a bit of a think about it and he said, 'Yeah, well, I guess that's another way yer could go about it.'

Another story Drewie told us ... see, on the other side of Urunga there's a big steel bridge over the Bellinger River and at this time there was a mob of workmen sandblasting and repainting the bridge. Anyhow, all these schoolkids, they'd get on the train and they'd go to all the toilets and do their business but they wouldn't pull the chains. Then, just as the train hit the bridge, they'd pull the chains and *whoosh* it went all over the workmen. Drewie reckoned you could hear these fellers calling out from under the bridge, 'You little bastards!'

But I had all me bloody years on steam and, oh, they were great old days, and a lot of history, too. I remember I was in Junee when the 38-ers were running down there. I fired on them. Gee, they were a beautiful engine them big green fellers, the 38-ers.

But the railways are finished now. All the old blokes are disappearing and the humour's gone. Ever notice how nobody seems to laugh much these days? I used to have a bit of a laugh with one old mate from my railways days, but he's been put in a home down at Adamstown. He can't hear and he can't see, the poor old bugger. I used to fire for his dad and, when he come to Kempsey, he fired for me. Then there's another old railways bloke, he's been a mate of mine for sixty years now. He's near ninety but you wouldn't get much sense out of him. He's as mad as a shit-carter's horse.

Black Night

One time I was working out of Sydney, heading north to Murwillumbah, on the Gold Coast Motor Rail. It was a pretty plush sort of motor, you know, with air-conditioning, buffet, the works. Anyway, I always went through the train after Strathfield to make sure everything was okay. So I get to the vestibule end and there's this little Aboriginal girl, standing there in amongst all these business types. I mean, it'd be lucky if she was sixteen years of age, and she had a tiny tot with her, a tiny baby. Well, this kid looked terrified, and it was a really shit winter's night. We'd had ferocious storms, trees blown down and stuff, and this little girl, she said to me, she said, 'Can you help me, please?'

'How can I help you, love?' I asked.

She said, 'The conductor said he's gonna throw me off at Hornsby 'n' make me go on the North Coast Mail.'

Now, the North Coast Mail was an atrocious train. Every sleaze in town got on that thing, plus it stopped at every tin-pot town along the way, so it took twice as long to get anywhere.

So I said to this girl, 'Why does he want to throw you off the train?'

'Because I haven't got a seat,' she said.

Now, what the conductor had said was complete crap, see, because what a lot of people used to do was buy a ticket north, get on the Gold Coast Motor Rail and stand in the vestibule just like these business-types mob had done. Then, after Hornsby, when things had settled down, the conductor would come along and find them a seat. Anyhow, this girl, she's got her ticket and she's going home to Grafton. So I looked around and I saw a vacant seat and I said, 'Look, there's a seat. You sit in there with your baby.'

'It's not my baby,' she said.

It could've been her sister's kid for all I know. But the little baby was terrified, too, you know, and I just couldn't let them get kicked off like that.

'Well,' I said, 'as of now, it is your baby. Look,' I said, 'there's no way in the world you're getting chucked off this train on a night like this, especially when you see all these other people standing around, waiting to be given a seat.'

Like, you know, these business people had no more right to be on the train than she did. What's the priorities, eh? But I had to be careful not to compromise my job, so I said, 'Now, can you cry?'

She said, 'What do yer mean?'

I said, 'Well, I can't do much in my position with the railways, but,' I said, 'the moment they go to remove you, burst into tears, and tell them you won't take your baby off the train, in weather like this.' I said, 'I'll wait up the other end and if I see that they've thrown you off, I'll just pull the power on the train and you can have my seat.'

See, they gave us a special seat allocation and, as far as I was concerned, she could have my seat and I'd ride the van. That didn't worry me. I didn't mind standing up for that kid, you know.

And she said, 'Will yer, really?'

'Yes,' I said, 'but you've gotta do your bit, too.'

So I left her there and, when I was walking back up, I bumped into the conductor. I mean, the bastard was an absolute bloody pisspot. The prick got the sack later anyway, for being drunk on the job. So I said to him, 'How're you going?'

'Fuck it,' he said, 'I've got some black moll down the back who wants a fucking seat so I'm gettin' her chucked off at Hornsby. She can go on the North Coast Mail fer all I care.'

'Oh really,' I said, 'then what about all these other people who are standing around?'

'Oh,' he said, 'I'll find seats for them. No problem there.'

So when we pulled into Hornsby, I stuck my head out the door to keep an eye on things. Then along come all these railway officials, you know, and the stationmaster's there. So we're waiting and I didn't see her get out. Next thing, up goes the green flag and the green light and away we go. So I wandered back down to see how the little kid was going and I bumped into the conductor again.

'What happened?' I asked.

'You wouldn't believe it,' he said. 'The black bitch burst into fuckin' tears and so all the officials said, "Well, you just stay right there, darling" and they walked off and now I'm stuck with her.'

'Well,' I said, 'that's a bit of bad luck.'

Anyway, I go down and there she is, sitting in a seat—she's still trembling—and I said, 'Now, how're you going? Has he given you a seat?'

'Not really,' she said. 'He just walked off without sayin' anythin'.'

'Well,' I said, 'you've got your bottom in this one, keep it there. Now,' I said, 'have you or that baby been fed?'

And she said, 'Well, actually, no.'

So I went down and I saw the catering girls and when I told them what'd happened they said, 'You're kidding!'

'No, I'm not,' I said.

'Well, that's disgraceful,' they said, 'and what's more, that bastard of a conductor better not think he's coming in here for a meal tonight.' Then they said, 'Now, where is she?'

So I told them and I offered to pay for the meal.

'No you won't,' the girls said. 'We'll look after things.'

Anyway, those catering girls, they took a tray down to her and they fed her, they fed the baby and, oh, that little girl got limo-service right up until she got off at Grafton.

'Bloody Victorians'

Me and a mate, we'd come by train all the way over from Melbourne to Perth to have a look at a couple of properties down at Albany. Back in those days it was a hell of a trip—I'm talking late 1950s here—and when we'd reached Perth we had a bit of a stink with our return bookings. See, I'm sure something shonky was going on because when we asked the booking clerk if he could get us on a train back to Adelaide the following week, he muttered something about 'bloody Victorians' and told us bluntly that the train was fully booked—that is, unless we had a spare twenty quid.

'Not on yer life,' we said.

Anyhow, we told a taxi driver about this and he said, 'Have yer thought about going home by boat?' Which we hadn't. So he dropped us off at the P&O office in Perth where a young male clerk, about seventeen years old, explained that a migrant ship was due in Fremantle in about five days that was heading to Melbourne.

'Can we get on it?' we asked.

'Not sure,' he said. 'Give me a ring in a couple'a days.'

'Okay,' we said. Then we took the train down to Albany to inspect the properties which, mind you, we never took up.

So a couple of days later we called the P&O clerk and he said that there were two berths available on this migrant ship and if we could pay ten shillings each he'd reserve them for us.

'But we're down in Albany,' we explained, 'and there's no way we can get the money to you.'

'Well, no money, no booking,' he said.

But after some friendly coercion, this young feller finally agreed to pay the money out of his own pocket. Now, this was an extremely generous offer because back in them days twenty shillings was a hell of a lot of money, especially for a youngster just starting out. Anyhow, we thanked him profusely and we assured him that we'd be at the P&O office as soon as our train arrived in Perth, on the morning after next.

So the following afternoon, we jumped on the train at Albany for our return journey. The train was one of those very early model diesel-electric locomotives. It was about half an hour late departing but that was okay. We still had a bit of time up our sleeve. Then, when we got going we settled into our seats and we knocked the top off a few bottles of grog and shared them around with all and sundry in the carriage, which lightened everyone's mood. So everything went to schedule, that was, until about nine o'clock that night when, suddenly, all the lights went out and the train gradually came to a halt.

'What the hell's going on?' I said to me mate.

We could still hear the diesel motor running so we just sat there in complete darkness, waiting for the lights to come back on. But they didn't. Then when I took a look out the window I saw the train guard coming down the track with his lantern and the driver coming up the track with his lantern and, as it happened, they met just outside my window.

'What's up?' the guard asked.

'She's fucked,' the driver replied.

'What do yer mean, "she's fucked"?'

'I mean exactly what I said,' said the driver.

'So how long do yer reckon it'll take yer to get her going?'

'Wouldn't have a fuckin' clue,' the driver replied, then he went on to explain that it'd be difficult for us to go anywhere because, while the diesel engine was okay, the electrics part of the loco had burnt out and, without the electrics, she couldn't go.

By this stage me and me mate were getting quite concerned that we'd not only miss the boat but the poor kid who'd paid the twenty shillings for our booking would also be thinking that he was well out of pocket. So we jumped down onto the tracks and told the guard and the driver how we had to be in Perth early next morning. Well, they couldn't have cared less. They reckoned they had enough on their plate without having to worry about two 'bloody Victorians', as they called us.

Anyhow, eventually, the guard came to the conclusion that the railways had never been the same since the 'good old steam days' and he'd had enough of all this new fan-dangled machinery. So, he was going to get on the telephone he had down the back and contact 'the powers that be' and let them sort the 'bloody mess' out. We all accompanied the guard back to his van where he produced an old field-type telephone that had two wire leads to which two small alligator clips had been attached.

'Okay, then,' he said to me. 'You want'a get to Perth urgently so get up that pole and fasten these clips onto the wires.'

Well, he only had an old kerosene wick-type railway lamp which, in the dark, was completely bloody useless. I couldn't even see the wires up the telephone pole. Anyway, I put the two clips in my mouth and me mate bunked me up until I stood on his shoulders. By the light of the moon I could just make out the crossbar above my head, so I cuddled the pole with my knees and hands and, with as much strength as a bloke who had a few grogs on board could muster, I dragged myself up until I could just reach the overhead lines. Then, by hanging on by my knees and one hand, I managed to attach both the alligator clips before I slid back down the pole and fell into a crumpled heap at the bottom. The guard then mumbled a few choice words under his breath—probably about 'bloody Victorians'—turned the handle on the telephone, got a connection, and he found out that a goods steam loco was coming up behind us and it'd give us a shunt along.

'Okay then, that's all sorted,' the guard said. Then he looked at me and said, 'Up the pole again and unclip the wires.'

'Bullshit,' I said, and I grabbed the two wires and gave them a swift yank and off they came.

When he reeled in the wires, one of the alligator clips had gone missing in the dark. 'What about the bloody clip?' the guard said, and then he started whingeing about how the cost of the missing clip would be deducted from his wages. And on and on he went until the driver reminded him that the steam train would soon be coming up behind us and we'd be in a hell of a mess if we didn't put out the detonators to warn it that we were ahead. The driver then decided to return to the locomotive, as per the instruction book, because he said that's where he should be in cases like this.

'Righto,' the guard said to me and me mate, 'youse blokes come with me and carry this box of detonators. Count 500 yards,' he said and we stumbled off in the dark, back down the track in the direction of where the steam loco would be approaching. When we got to about 500 yards, the guard took two detonators out of the box and he placed one on each rail, opposite each other. Then we turned around and we headed back towards our train and counted 400 yards before he set another two detonators on each rail. A final set of detonators were placed about 10 foot from his guard's van.

'Okay,' said the guard, 'you fellers get back on the train, the loco'll be here any tick now.' The guard then returned to his van, as per the instruction book, because he said that's where he should be in cases like this.

Well, we waited and we waited. Then, some two or three hours later we finally heard a steam train coming in the distance and, what's more, it sounded like it was going full bore. *Bang!* The first set of detonators went off. Now, I had it in mind that the driver of the steam train would stop and the two crews would get together and have a bit of a yarn before he shunted us on. But not bloody likely. In fact the steamer sounded like it was picking up speed. There came a whistle blast and *Bang!* as the next set of detonators exploded. And still it sounded like he was picking up pace, so much so that all us passengers gripped hard onto our seats in expectation. *Bang!* went the last set of detonators, immediately followed by a *Crash!* as the steam loco hit us.

Well, there were almighty screams all round as we thought we'd been hit from behind by a train travelling at full pelt. And by Jesus, I reckoned we'd been hit a mile too hard too, though I suppose the steam loco driver wanted to use as much of his own momentum as possible to get us on the move. And move we did.

Anyhow, we finally arrived in Perth about four hours late. By that stage we were in a hell of a panic, though not as bad as the poor young P&O clerk who, by that time, thought he'd done his dough. So we paid him, thanked him profusely, grabbed our tickets, jumped on the next train to Fremantle, and we arrived at the dockside just as the wharfies were removing the gangway. And the buggers wouldn't put it back. No fear. 'Bloody Victorians,' they said, and they made us jump the last four feet to get on board, carrying our suitcases and all.

Boo

Oh, I loved trains ever since I was a kid. I always wanted to join the railways, you know, but because of my poor eyesight I knew I'd never be able to join Queensland Railways. So the next best thing was the cane trains. So I did an apprenticeship as a boilermaker and, once I done me time, I ended up getting a firing position at Millaquin Sugar Mill. Then you had to do a minimum of 1000 hours' firing before you could get your steam ticket to drive. So I passed my steam ticket and I started driving.

Now, the cane trains, they're the small ones that run on two-foot gauge tracks. They were sort of like a scaled-down version of a steam loco, built by Fowler's and Perry, in Adelaide. At Millaquin Sugar Mill, we had steam right up until about August 1975, then they brought up the E.M. Baldwin bogie locomotives to replace the steam. But they had a lot of failures with them, so about six or seven weeks of the year, we'd end up back on the steam locos. That lasted till about '79, and by that time they'd truly lived their life.

Anyhow, my story's about a driver we had at the Millaquin Sugar Mill, an old chappie by the name of Ronny Cook. Now, Ronny's nerves were so shot, you know, that if you said, 'Boo' he'd jump a mile high. Oh, he used to shake like hell. Every time we stopped, he'd swallow a Bex powder to try and settle his nerves. Then, also to settle down his nerves, he'd try to roll a smoke. The only trouble was, he'd still be shaking that much that he'd be spraying his tobacco left, right and centre, and more of it'd end up on the bloody ground than what ended up in his cigarette.

But there was this church, you see. And one day Ronny and another guy, Wayne Heidke, they went up to this particular line at St John's Road. Now, I don't know if you've been there or not, but the cane track crosses Elliots Road and, on the left-hand side, going out, there's this old church—St John's Lutheran Church. Anyhow, Ronny always used to get the jitters extremely bad when he was up that way because he was convinced that this church was haunted, which, of course, did nothing for his already fragile nervous condition.

So they were up there one night. It was a full moon and they were shunting empties around and Wayne was way back down at the end of the train—the 'rake' as we call it. The next thing, he sees Ronny running around like a cut chook, uncoupling the No. 6 steam loco and he takes off on it—he just bolted. So then, this Wayne Heidke took off after Ronny to try and find out what'd happened. Anyway, Wayne ended up having to run all the way back to the mill, which was a fair bloody way, and when he finally caught up with Ronny, he reckoned that Ronny was so shook up that he was trying to down Bex powders and roll cigarettes, all at the same time.

So Wayne said, 'Ronny, what happened back there?'

And Ronny swore black and blue that he'd heard the devil calling out to him from over in the church.

'Don't be bloody silly,' Wayne said, 'all it was, was someone playin' the friggin' organ.'

Call Boy

I grew up in beautiful uptown Cootamundra, population 6600, the home of the Cootamundra wattle—or, to give it its botanic name, *Acacia baileyana*—and also the birthplace of the late Sir Donald Bradman. Correct: 89 Adams Street was where the Bradmans lived. In another job, as a telegram boy, I had the pleasure of delivering a telegram to the Don's mum.

Cootamundra is a rail town on the main line between Sydney and Melbourne. Now, at night, especially in winter, the air in Cootamundra was incredibly still. Nothing moved. No leaves. Nothing. And you might think that those conditions would make for a perfect night's sleep, but no, because approximately 23 kilometres south-west of Cootamundra is what's colloquially known as the Bethungra Loop. To give its correct title, it's the Bethungra Rail Spiral. Now, the Bethungra Loop is a unique engineering feat in as much as there were two different railway tracks—southbound, towards Melbourne, and northbound, towards Sydney—

and they worked their way through some of the deepest rail cuttings in Australia as they crisscrossed each other in corkscrew fashion, around Bethungra Hill.

And because of the depth of these cuttings, sounds became amplified. An example: say you were new to town, you'd be in bed and it'd be dead quiet. You'd just nod off then you'd hear a train coming up from the south. You'd hear it slow down through Cootamundra. And then, when you heard it leave town, you'd think, 'Well, the train's gone, now I can get back to sleep.'

But no, no, no, because the train had only disappeared around the back side of Bethungra Hill. And when it returned around the town side of the hill, bugger me, it sounded like it was coming back towards you again. Then it'd disappear. Then it'd reappear. And that'd continue till the train got out of the loop.

So you can imagine that, with trains coming and going at all hours it was quite manic until you got used to it. And that's how you could tell who the newcomers to town were because they were the ones who walked around the place in a dazed state, with their eyes half hanging out, due to lack of sleep, or Bethungra Loop-itis you could call it.

Anyhow, Cootamundra was the place of my first job. It was with the New South Wales Government Railways, and that particular job had the inglorious title of 'Call Boy'. One part of our responsibilities was that, when a train was due, we had to race down from the railway station on our pushbikes to shut the railway crossing gates at the main road. There were four gates.

Two each side. Then once the train had passed, we opened the gates and allowed the traffic to go through.

I don't remember how much I got paid but, as I recall, the shift was twelve hours, say, 6 pm till 6 am. All we had was a state government-issue pushbike that had little battery-operated lights. And we stayed at the station overnight in a tiny room with a little coke fire burner— it would've been too bloody cold otherwise—and we weren't supposed to sleep. We weren't paid to sleep.

The other part of a call boy's responsibilities was to assign train duties to the guards, drivers and firemen. How it worked was that, in the station, we had a house plan of every worker's house so we knew where his bedroom window was, and it was a condition of employment that he leave that bedroom window ajar. Then an hour or so before his train was due to leave, we'd go out on our pushbike, wake them up, tell them where their train was in the yard, what time it was leaving and where it was going to, then we'd return to the station to be given our next job.

Now, the most memorable occasion for me as a call boy was when I went around to a young guard's place one night to give him a call. This was in winter. The air was incredibly still. Nothing moved—no leaves, nothing. And all was silent, until I arrived at his window to be greeted by a cacophony of sounds emanating from his bedroom, which definitely weren't sounds of the snoring variety. Of course, being young and imaginative, I put two and two together and equated it to the graphic descriptions I'd heard about when two people were having wild and intimate sex.

Anyhow, me being the impish devil I was, I decided to wait until the absolute crucial moment. Then, with split-second timing, I rapped loudly on his window, yelled out at the top of me voice, 'Train's in shed six. Yer off 'ta Narrandera in an hour.'

Then I bolted back to the station on my bike, where I duly made myself scarce because I knew there'd be a certain guard in a none too happy or satisfied mood, wanting to strangle a certain call boy.

Changing Times

When I was young I lived beside the rail line at Oxley, near Brisbane, and, as most boys did, I became interested in trains. I remember there was one steam train that used to arrive on the siding, behind our house, at six every morning and I'd always be up to watch it shunt. That was in about 1945, and it'd drop off coal hoppers and cattle for Hutton's Factory. Hutton's used the cattle to make 'camp pie' and all that sort of stuff. So they'd drop the coal hoppers off and about fifty head of cattle, then a couple of drovers would take the cattle 3 mile or so, up across the main Ipswich Highway, up to the factory. And it may seem odd but twenty years later, I was either firing or driving that particular train myself.

I joined the railways in 1955 as a locomotive cleaner. Then after a month or so I did what was known as a Fire's Test and after passing that I was qualified to look after locos in the steam sheds. See, after the locos had finished a run they'd store them in a shed and our job was to keep sufficient water in the boiler and a reasonable fire in the box, without causing them to raise steam. Then the fireman would come along and he'd get half an hour to prepare the engine for its next trip.

I was twenty-two by then and, on the 11 pm shift, there'd be three of us and we'd have about twenty locomotives to look after. Then, to qualify as a fireman, you had to learn all the rules of the 'road'—the term we used for the track—that's the signals, safe working and so forth, plus you had nine types of locomotives and you had to learn the differences of them. Like, some had square fireboxes. Some were long narrow fireboxes. You had to learn all that. There was no 'on-the-job manual training', so it was all done in your own time. Then after qualifying, you were given one week on local yard, shunting engines, followed by two weeks on local goods, then you could be required to work suburban passenger, fast mail trains, heavy goods or whatever they put you on.

So you'd be with a different driver every day and you'd rely on them to teach you the finer points of firing; that is, to avoid too much black smoke, to keep the boiler just under full pressure so the safety valves didn't blow off—wasting water—to learn what to look out for on your side of the loco and repeating all the signals to the driver. Then after you'd been firing for a while you usually teamed up with a regular driver.

Now I teamed up with an old driver named Mick, as his fireman, and right from the start we hit it off. Mick was a happy sort of bloke. Even if we started at three o'clock in the morning he'd arrive with a big smile and suggest that, when I got a minute, I might put the billy in the fire and make a cup of tea. A cuppa was the main thing early in the morning.

But, see, in the late '50s, when the diesels were first arriving on the scene, the older drivers weren't required to learn how to drive them. My first job with Mick, as a diesel driver, was one I won't forget. It was the Rockhampton Mail, out of Roma Street at about eight o'clock at night, and right from the start it was obvious that Mick had little idea of the speed we were travelling. See, after you shut off, diesels didn't hang back like the steam engines did. Like, when you're freewheeling on a steam engine you usually run at, say, 25 mph, around a particular curve. But, with this diesel, Mick was hitting these curves at 40 mph. So it was really running away on him and he had a few emergency brake applications. Then, when judging coming into the stations, he ended up being either too short or too far over the ends.

I left Mick after I passed my driving exam in 1963. Then I did a lot of work either in the shed or stabling engines, or working suburban and goods and passengers and, when necessary, also camp-away jobs to places like Gympie and Toowoomba. But, like Mick, I always preferred the steam engines because the driver and the fireman and the engine all worked as a team. If any of them was slipping up, you'd all have a bad day. Like, if the engine wasn't steaming, there'd be trouble. If the driver was using too much steam or water, the fireman would have a bad time. If the fireman wasn't keeping the steam up, well, the driver had a bad time. You all had to work together. That was the joy of it.

Anyhow, like a lot of the older fellers, right from the start, it was obvious old Mick didn't have the feel for the diesels. Then, unfortunately, he had a couple of fatal accidents. I don't think I should go into graphic details about what actually happened, but the result was that a couple of people were killed. I mean, they weren't really his fault but the courts tried to make it out that way and it really knocked Mick around. Then, through the stress of the court cases, his eyesight went on him, through diabetes. So they gave him a job in the boardroom, allocating engines onto their next job. But, of course, he never quite adjusted to that either because old Mick was a steam engine man, through and through—nothing more, nothing less. And that was that.

Dead Drunk

I'm eighty-six in October and it's twenty-one years since I retired from the railways. What happened was that, during the war, I was in New Guinea and Borneo and, when that finished, I come to Parkes and someone said they were looking for cleaners up at the loco depot. Cleaning's like, you black-oil the steam engines then rub it in with cotton waste. It's like polishing your boots, which was something I'd done a heck of a lot of during the war. So I was cleaning for a while, then they sent me down to Sydney for an exam. That's how I passed the acting fireman's job.

Then from acting fireman I went to a fireman. Then I went for an acting driver and finally, I passed for driver. We used to run to Orange, to Cootamundra, freight to Dubbo, then we'd run out through Euabalong West, where we'd camp in the barracks, before going on to Ivanhoe the next day.

But there was a railways chap I remember; they called him 'Eggy' because his name was Eggleston, and this

Eggy was a real drinker. My God, he could drink. And probably because nobody could put up with him and his drinking, that's why he remained single. Anyhow, Eggy lived in a room out there in the railway barracks and he had this big black dog he called 'Smart Dog'. So Eggy came home this night as full as a boot and he found the dog sleeping in his bed, so he said, 'Come on, Smart Dog, get off.'

And Smart Dog started growling at him, so Eggy said, 'Yer worse than a bloody wife you are, Smart Dog.' And he grabbed a blanket and he went and slept on the couch while his dog stayed in his bed.

Then another time he drank so much that he poisoned himself with the alcohol. He was that bad that he was comatose and he needed to see a doctor. So they put him on one of those trolley things that the porters used to carry all the luggage around on. Anyhow, they wheeled him out of the barracks and up onto the railway platform and, because he was still out to it, they just threw a sheet over him and left him lying there, on this trolley, while they went to get the doctor.

Anyhow, it just so happened that while they were away, two old women came walking along the platform and they saw this porter's trolley, and they could see that under the sheet was this human body. Anyway, one old woman said to the other, 'Oh, it's such a terrible thing to leave a corpse just laying out on the platform like that.'

'Yes,' said the other, 'God rest this poor lost soul.'

Then they both started to cross themselves and mutter their silent prayers to departed spirits or whatever, and while they were muttering away and crossing themselves Eggy suddenly let out a pitiful groan from under the sheet.

Well, you should've seen those two old ducks. They thought they'd raised the dead.

Dennis the Menace

I'm coming up to seventy-six and I'm determined to continue to make everyone's life miserable for at least another twenty-four years. That's my goal. Anyway, I was born in Adelaide and we went to live out on the east–west railway line, virtually straightaway. My father was a ganger, in charge of a maintenance gang, on the Nullarbor. So we went out to what they call the old 298 Mile, just out of Tarcoola. We were there for a few years, then we went to Zanthus. That's where I went to school. A lot of people say to me, 'Hey, Alf, where did yer go to school?'

So I puff out me chest and I say, 'Zanthus Tech.'

'Oh, geez,' they say, 'you must'a had a good education, then.'

See, they don't realise that Zanthus was a little bloody town, out in the middle of nowhere. It's exactly 137 miles east of Kalgoorlie and, I might add, it's the prettiest little railway siding on the east–west line, big gum trees, the lot. Now, I'm not sure how many people would've been living there back then. I'm talking about the early 1940s, you know. But I do know that there were seventeen of us kids at the school; though, in saying that, you've got to remember that some of the families had five or six children. And the whole time we were there, apart from your usual sorts of scraps, there was never any big arguments, neither family arguments nor between us kids. Us kids mucked about amongst ourselves very happily. We even went out and played with the kids from Cundeelee Aboriginal Mission, which was about 25 miles north, and they also came in and we all played together. There was never any problems.

But I always loved trains, right from back when I can remember, and at Zanthus they used to do a bit of shunting—you know, water, general, whatever—and the crews always gave us kids a ride on the train around the triangle. They'd show us how to fire and all that. Oh, they were wonderful. Though there was one incident, I might as well tell you. You know how there's always some little 'Dennis the Menace' in every place. Well, that was me. And out of the seventeen of us kids that were at school in Zanthus, there was one particular mate of mine, Donny Mitchell. Now, Donny was a bit of a Dennis the Menace, too. We were both about eight and, if anything happened in the camp, we'd be the first ones to face court. What's more, more often than not, we were usually found guilty as charged.

Anyhow, on this particular occasion a bullion train stopped at Zanthus on its way through. Old Kiwi Walters was the stationmaster back then. Of course, every train that came through was an occasion. But, with this being a bullion train, it was an even bigger occasion than normal. Of course, all us kids went down there to see this train. There were three or four armed guards hanging about on the platform, which was exciting, so me and Donny, we started asking them about what sort of guns they had, and how much bullion was on the train, and had they ever been robbed, and how many robbers they'd shot dead and all that. So they were sitting there with their guns, very relaxed, chatting away to us and I had a thought, so I said to Donny, 'Donny, come with me.'

'Okay,' he said and so we went down to what was called the 'trolley shed'. The trolley shed was where my father kept all the maintenance gear, and he kept his section car, and also that's where he kept his detonators; you know, those explosive things they used as warning devices on the railways.

So Donny and me, we got four detonators and we went back to the train. But instead of going up the platform side, we crept along the other side of the train—the blind side, where nobody could see us. Then we placed these detonators under the wheels of the bullion train. Next thing, the guard blows his whistle and gives the right-of-way and the train starts to move. Then, *Bang! Bang! Bang! Bang!* Off go these detonators. Then the train screeched to a halt, and, bloody hell, I didn't realise there were so many armed guards looking after that bullion. There were blokes coming out of windows, blokes coming out of doors. Guns were aimed left, right and centre, and poor old Kiwi Walters, the stationmaster, shot out of his office so fast that he banged himself on the door and nearly broke his bloody arm.

'Blimey,' I said to Donny, 'we'd better get out'a here.'

See, I just thought it'd be all a bit of a joke and that these armed guard fellers would know the difference between an exploding detonator and a hold-up gun. But apparently they didn't. So Donny and me, we took off. Then, after the train finally left, they did a round-up of all the kids and there were two missing, me and Donny, and that's how they found out who the culprits were.

Anyhow, my father was a very strict man so I got a hell of a hiding and I was sent to bed without dinner. But then, later that night, I heard all the men talking over a few beers in our kitchen and, oh, they were laughing and going on. Oh, they just thought it was a hell of a joke.

Dust Storm

Right throughout Australia, farming on the fringes has always been fraught with danger. With the poorer soil quality, rural life can so easily be turned into a natural disaster when hit by drought, flood, plague or whatever. Now, I'm not sure if this incident actually came under the official category of a natural disaster but, in all my time with the railways, I'd never been so afraid when the elements turned nasty.

It must've been 1953 or '54. I know it was late autumn because the farmers had already prepared their land for seeding. As our little RX loco headed out from the city, a strong westerly started to blow, causing some of the loose topsoil to become airborne. The guard that day was a fellow by the name of Dick Till, the driver was Jimmy Martin, and his fireman-mate was a New Australian whom we called George, to save confusion.

By the time we arrived at Apamurra, this westerly had fast turned the sky into an ominous dark cloud of sandy-soil. Then while we were shunting, the gale hit with a vengeance. What's more, the stinging dust became thicker and thicker until it reached the point where it was impossible for the loco crew to see our hand signals. Even the signal lamp was useless because, as soon as we lit it, it blew out.

We then became worried that someone might get killed if we carried on in such conditions so we shunted the loco back onto the remainder of the train, where we abandoned operations and scurried for safety into the little weatherboard and corrugated iron stationmaster's office. At that time Max Isted was the stationmaster, so the five of us huddled inside listening to the wind roar and wail. Now, to give you some idea, such was the force of this dust storm that the western wall of the building was actually bulging inwards. It was frightening. What's more, the storm showed no signs of abating.

We were wondering what the hell was going to happen next when, above the racket, we heard someone hammering on the door, on the eastern side of the building. When we managed to open it, in burst a little fellow, a minister of religion, who was absolutely distraught. Oh, he was totally beside himself. He was crying, blabbering, incoherent. Still, we finally pacified him enough to hear how his car had become stuck in drift-sand on the level crossing just north of the station and, worse still, his wife had remained in the car and she was petrified.

Anyhow, this priest knew that a train was due so he'd staggered along the railway tracks in the blinding storm, hoping to stop the train should it appear out of the black void that engulfed him. So we were able to assure him that we were the crew of the train in question, and it certainly wasn't going anywhere because we'd abandoned it due to the conditions.

It soon became apparent that the storm was going to continue well into the night. All forms of communication were out, so we were stuck. We discussed our plight and it was decided that Max would battle over to his place, pick up his car and then drive us to the nearby hotel, where we'd stay the night. So Max disappeared into the whipping dust and eventually brought his little Ford Prefect to the station, where we all shielded ourselves from the onslaught and made a dash for his car. Then the trip to the hotel was an adventure in itself. Even with our accumulated weight, acting as ballast, Max was still fighting to keep the vehicle stable. So strong was the howling gale that we were slipping and slewing across the road. Anyhow, we made it to the pub and the storm gradually abated overnight. Now, such was the confusion that I can't exactly recall what happened to the priest; whether he staggered back out into the storm to return to his distraught wife or if Max somehow got him back down to the crossing.

Anyhow, before sun-up, Max returned and drove us back to the station. Everything was sanded up. The reversing wheel on the loco was stuck. Sand covered all the controls in the open-type cab and, when we opened the door of the brake van, such had been the power of the gale that pyramids of sandy-dust ran from the cracks in the door joints, right across the floor of the van.

The local ganger then arrived to tell us that there was a 3 feet deep sand-drift across the tracks, towards Milindella, which was where the priest's car had been stranded. When we asked, he told us that there was no sign of a car so we assumed all was well.

Anyhow, after the per-way gang had shovelled the sand from the track we were given the all clear and away we went. However, at the next little township the timber and iron from the roof of the wheat and barley stacks lay spread-eagled across the tracks and we were stranded once again. That was it, there'd be no train that day. So, without the facilities for turning the loco, we had to work the train back home, 'tender first'.

So, as I said, I'm not sure if that particular event was ever categorised as being a natural disaster but, now, here's something; remember how I told you that we were never sure about just what happened to the priest and his wife? Well, almost fifty years later, I was at a dinner and I overheard Eric Pietsch telling someone how, many years ago, he knew of a Lutheran pastor from around that area who'd gotten his car stuck in a huge dust storm on the railway line and how his wife had been trapped inside the car. Eric went on to say they'd eventually found their way to safety, but that the storm had been so intense that a lot of the paintwork had been stripped off the priest's car.

Elephant

I spent forty-two years with Victorian Railways and I've been retired twenty-one years. Hang on, that's wrong. My mind's a bit scratchy, these days. No, it'd be about twenty-five years since I retired. Something like that. Anyhow, I joined back in the late 1930s, when I was a lad, and I started sweeping platforms and cleaning toilets and all that and I rose through the ranks until I was made a stationmaster at the age of twenty-nine, and over my time I worked in about ten stations in all different parts around Victoria.

So I've done a lot and I've seen a lot, and something I've seen that I don't like is the way they've been closing so many of these railway lines and that, down. Why, here in Nhill there's no-one left to man the station and I don't think there's a manned station until Tailem Bend or Murray Bridge. All the signalling's gone automatic. These days there's this big switchboard thing at Ararat where they just turn the knobs and dials and it runs all the signals and tells the train drivers where to shunt and when to stop or to proceed, and it puts them on to No. 2 track, or wherever. And they're also in radio contact so they can ring the drivers and let them know when they're going to cross a train. Oh yes, she's all automatic these days.

See, they don't need people anymore. And that's something I don't like because, with the railways closing down, it also cut out a lot of the local jobs. It's no wonder that most of these country towns are in the doldrums. Well, just here in Nhill, the electricity commission closed their office and put off about six people. The post office has been privatised. There's no switchboard girls. And where they had about twelve fellers working in a gang, to fix up all the faults, now there's only two and there's more faults than there ever was. Then all the banks have amalgamated. It's a lot of people and that's everywhere.

See, back when I was with the railways, every country town I lived in, everything came to us by train: the groceries, the beer for the pub, the hospitals, chemist medicines, farm machinery, superphosphate, oil tankers, even the circus. Oh yes, I don't know about other states but here in Victoria, Wirth's Circus always travelled by train and, if there was enough room in the railway yards, they'd even hold the circus in there. That's true. When I was at Hamilton they held it right there in the railway yards, not far from the Grange Creek.

So anyhow, do you want to hear some stories about the circus and the railways? I've got three stories about elephants here. Are you ready? Okay, here we go. Well, the first story is that one of the elephants ate carrot fern—that's a weed—and it killed it. Yes, that's one story. Well, that's all there is to it. Carrot fern's poisonous, and the elephant ate it and it died. End of story.

The next elephant story happened when I was at Wycheproof. Wycheproof's another Mallee town. It's the only place in Victoria where the town's divided by the railway line, up the main street. Anyhow, one time, at Wycheproof, an elephant escaped from the circus and it took off and it knocked down these people's fence. Then it went into their back garden and trampled over everything—all their vegetables and their flowers—and it also knocked a full rainwater tank off the tank stand. So that's the second story.

Then there's a third one. Now, at Charlton—that's another place I worked at—Wirth's set up their circus next to the railway station, which was right near to the railway dam. Anyhow, it was as hot as hell so when one of the elephants saw the water, it broke its chains and it went straight into the dam for a drink and a wash and a muck around. The only trouble was that, when it was time for it to come out for the show, it wouldn't budge. I mean, they called out its name, but no. They offered it food, but no. They couldn't drag it out because it was too big, so that was no good. They couldn't use a stun gun or anything because if it was stunned it might've just gone 'flop' in the dam and drowned.

So they were stumped as to how to get this elephant out of the dam, see. Then one bright feller came up with an idea. He went and he got a really long electrical extension cord. Then he bared the wires of this extension cord at one end and he threw that end into the railway dam and the other end he went and he plugged into the power point over at the railway station. Anyway, when he shouted, 'Flick the switch!' a feller at the switchboard end turned the electricity on.

Now, I don't know if you've ever seen an elephant fly or not. Well, that day, I just about reckon I did. I tell you, that elephant, it squealed like buggery and it just about took off. And that's true, and that's how they got the elephant out of the railway dam. They gave him a bit of a charge, eh, by electrocuting the water. The only trouble was that, once the elephant shot out of the water, it still had its momentum up and it took off like greased lightning, straight past the circus tent, down the main street, and it was halfway to the next town before they even caught up with it.

Elvis

Well, we were from Sydney, originally, and my husband and I decided to come up to Port Augusta and he joined the railways. First he was just a fettler and he got the job at Neuroodla. Neuroodla was very nice. It was only about six or eight houses and they were very nice—you know, a lot of room and everything. I think they were made from weatherboard.

So we were at Neuroodla, then we went to Pimba, to Tent Hill, then back to Pimba. My husband was a ganger at Tent Hill and we had a petrol generator to make our own electricity. There was about eight houses there and the Tea and Sugar train come through every fortnight, so you'd put your order form in for your food and supplies and they'd drop it off on the way through.

Now, I think it was at Tent Hill; we had a dog and my youngest son, he was just walking so he must've been only about two. And, oh, that dog used to follow him around everywhere. But we never let the dog come inside the house with him. It was an outside dog. But

71

then, one day, I was in the kitchen. It was a very hot day and I knew that my son was in the lounge room. Then I heard the express coming so I looked around and my son wasn't in the house. He'd disappeared.

So I ran outside and, oh dear, I couldn't see him anywhere. By then I could see the train was coming through Tent Hill and by jingo, my heart had a flutter. Oh, I was calling out everywhere. I was just imagining him down there on the tracks and the train was running over him. So I ran over and I took a look at the train line. But no, I couldn't see him. I couldn't see the dog. So I ran back to the house—I was so frightened—and I looked everywhere for him, up and down and all around the place. And then, when I'd just about given up I went and sat on the outside steps and there he was, under the house, all curled up asleep with the dog. But jingo, that really put the wind up me.

Oh, can I just mention Pimba again. That's where I met my friend Shirley and her family. Shirley's a life-long friend but it was sad because just a couple of weeks ago she passed away. We did everything together, Shirley and me. I remember the time at Pimba when she forgot to give her son, Robert, his lunch and off to school he went without it. See, from Pimba they used to go up to school at Woomera in the bus. It was a nice day—a beautiful day, really—and Shirley come around and she said, 'Do you fancy a walk up to Woomera, I forgot Robert's lunch.'

So we left at about half past nine and I was pushing the stroller with my youngest son. I think I also had my daughter who would've been about three or something then, and I had another one of my sons with me. Woomera was a two- or three-hour walk away but they had all that security there, in the compound where the school was. Like, you had to be checked to go in and to go out and all that.

Anyway, we reckoned we'd easily get there by lunchtime so Robert could have his lunch. So we were just wandering along and chatting and stuff and mucking around with the kids and whatever. Oh, it was fun. But we must've somehow got too caught up in the day because just as we got to the school, well, it must've been about half past three because all the kids were finishing up. So then we came back to Pimba on the school bus and Robert had a late lunch on the way. But it was amazing just how easy time got away from you when you lived out in some of them little railway places out there.

Then did I mention Tarcoola? After a while we left Pimba and we went to Tarcoola. Tarcoola was quite big for us. There were about twenty houses there and, oh, they had everything. They had a shop and a pub and a little school, and they even had a shed there where they showed films every fortnight. It was the old reels of film back then. But this shed was kind of fairly big, but not too big, and it was made of tin and there were wooden seats and, I think, the floor might've been concrete.

But the film I most remember was the first time I ever saw Elvis Presley. Well, I used to like listening to Elvis singing on the wireless, but when I seen him up there in person, I thought, 'Wow. Oh, how lovely.' I just thought he was marvellous. And it was just like he'd come all the way out to Tarcoola just to sing to me. And I just went … oh, you know what I mean … I just swooned—well, not swooned, but sort of like that. I just thought he was so marvellous. Oh yes, I loved Elvis Presley. I still do.

Glenn Ridge

Well, I guess my only claim to fame with the railways was being on the Glenn Ridge television show after they were filming on the IP (Indian Pacific) while I was driving the train over west. Oh, quite often some film mob or other comes up, mainly from overseas, doing travel shows. Probably over the years I've had my picture taken about 40,000 times by Japanese tourists and that, but you never see a picture, you know. So that was the first time I saw myself and I nearly missed out on that, too. Luckily someone rang up and said, 'Hey, Paul, they've got the IP on TV.' And I switched on the telly and there I was, as large as life. I think everyone in Australia saw it except my wife.

But as to how I got into the railways; well, I was originally a boilermaker and both my brother-in-law and father-in-law were engine drivers, so I thought I'd give it a go. Those days it was a five-year apprenticeship and you had to work with a driver for twelve months before you did six months driving under tuition. Then you could drive, though you weren't allowed to do crosses until you'd done an assessment.

Crosses are when you cross another train on a main line. See, on the main lines you've got crossing loops that go through a lot of the little sidings and one train has to pull in there to let the other one go through. A senior driver always did the crosses and, as an assistant driver, you had to get down and physically open a set of switches to get into the loop. In the city it's all automatic but, out where I worked—up the narrow gauge and out the east–west on the IP—there was none of that.

Well, the narrow gauge was the old Ghan line to Alice Springs. So it was the standard four foot, eight-and-a-half inch gauge to Marree, then they'd off-load all the containers onto three foot, six-inch narrow-gauge vehicles and we'd hop on a narrow-gauge engine. The crews used to work it up to the Alice in relays; seven and a half hours on, seven and a half hours off, continuous. The trip used to take about six to eight days, depending on which train you were on. If you were driving the 'slow mix', well, that'd service every fettler's camp and little siding, all the way up. It was sort of like trolling along on an old boat. That's how slow it was. Then you'd get to Alice and you generally had a night or two off before you turned around and came back again—that's if you didn't get a washaway, of course. If that happened, you'd be stuck.

A washaway's when the track gets washed away. I remember one time when Lake Eyre South was lapping alongside the track. Anyhow, we worked an empty train with flat tops up to Albury Creek, which is about three or four sidings up from Marree. They had a bit of a cutting there and the rail workers, they had a couple of front-end loaders, and everything else they needed, and they loaded us up with rocks and we took them up to Lake Eyre South, where they were building a bit of a levee wall so the water wouldn't wash away the tracks. Six of us went up that time. There were four drivers and two guards and we worked in relay. We slept and ate in a brake van. I think we did about three trips a day, you know, and we done that until they had things under control.

Anyhow, I remember how there were all these dead fish along the shore. They were freshwater fish that'd been washed down into the lake and the salt water had killed them. They were only about 3 or 4 inches long, and on a full moon you'd see all of these dead fish shining in the light. It was like a 2-foot-wide silver band going all around the shoreline.

But the birds ... oh, you just can't imagine. There were seagulls, pelicans, everything. And these birds had travelled thousands of kilometres, just to get there. I don't know how they got the news that there was a feed of fish so far away. Perhaps they've got a bird newspaper or radio—'Newsflash. Newsflash. Plenty of fish in Lake Eyre.' And they'd say, 'Let's go, fellers.' I don't know how it works. I think they're still trying to find out. But it must be built into their genes somehow. Perhaps they feel the pressure change in the air which lets them know it's raining up north and they can work out when the floodwater's coming down. It's amazing really, isn't it? Nature's such an amazing thing.

I think Glenn Ridge also did some filming around there. He's good. Have you ever seen him?

Gone Fishing

For twenty-six years I was the stage manager on the Western District Exhibit at the Sydney Royal Show, and the man in charge of the exhibit was a feller called Arthur Dreeves. Anyhow, Arthur was an old railways engineman from way back and, oh, he could tell a story or two.

I remember him telling me about one of his first trips as a fireman. Being new to the job, Arthur was determined to impress the driver, a very experienced and stern sort of chap. So they left Sydney with two 36 Class engines on their trip to pull one of the western mail trains over the Blue Mountains, before they went down the Great Zig-Zag, into the Lithgow Valley, and out onto the western plains. Anyhow, as they were going across Emu Plains, heading for the mountains, the driver said to Arthur, 'Now, Arthur, stoke her up because we'll need a full head of steam to get over the mountains.'

'Okay,' said Arthur.

Well, in the cabin of those old steam trains you had a bar on the floor that operated the opening and closing of the steel doors to the firebox. The coal tender's situated straight behind. So, what you did was, you shovelled the coal from the tender, swung around, put your foot on the bar, the steel doors opened, you threw the coal in, you took your foot off the bar and the doors shut closed so that the heat was maintained in the firebox until you got another shovelful of coal.

Anyhow, as I said, Arthur was out to make a really good impression on this driver and that's what he was doing. Things were going well and the two 36 Class engines were building up a good head of steam to tackle the approaching mountains. So, for the umpteenth time, Arthur got a big shovelful of coal, swung around and slammed his foot on the bar but, this time, as the doors came open, his foot slipped off the bar and the doors slammed shut again. Bang went the whole shovelful of coal, into the front of the closed steel doors. Arthur reckoned that, when the shovel hit the steel door, it jarred him to the bottom of his back teeth. Of course, big lumps of coal flew all over the floor of the cab.

'Silly bastard,' the driver mumbled. 'Wake up to yerself.'

Well, by this stage, with all the tension and the shovelling he'd done, Arthur was sort of getting a little bit lathered up with sweat. 'I'll show him,' he thought, so he swung around, got another big shovelful, stamped on the bar with all his might and heaved the coal into the firebox. And he said, 'And in she went, into the firebox, bloody shovel and all.'

'Well,' he said, 'I stood there like a stunned mullet, looking down at me empty hands then I took a look in the firebox.'

And, sure enough, his worst fears were confirmed—there was the shovel slowly melting down. Anyhow, he took a look at the driver and the driver didn't say a word, not one word. 'But,' Arthur reckoned, 'if looks could kill, I'd 'a been dead.' So then he quietly grabbed the fire bucket and, from there on, all the way up the Blue Mountains and down the Great Zig-Zag into Lithgow, he filled the firebox with the bucket.

Another story Arthur told me was when he was living at Oberon and working out of Bathurst. So Bathurst was his main station. Now, I guess this one must've also been way back in the late 1940s, early '50s, because things were pretty free and easy in the railways. Anyhow, by this stage Arthur had been promoted to a driver—don't ask me how—and he got the orders that him and his fireman mate had to take a loco way out near Bourke, to a place called Byrock, to pick up a load of sheep. What's more, they had to be there by two o'clock Saturday afternoon and all they had to do was to hook on the stock trucks, which were to be already loaded, and bring them back to Bathurst.

'Easy,' said Arthur.

Now, both Arthur and his fireman were pretty keen fishermen, you see, so Arthur said to his mate, 'Look, we're not rostered on for a couple'a days so why don't we take the loco out tomorrow, nice and early. We'll go out to Bourke, do a bit of fishing, and get back to Byrock by two o'clock Saturday afternoon to pick up these stock trucks and no bugger'll be the wiser.'

So that's what they did. Sunrise, they stoked her up and away they went, up to Bourke, to do a spot of fishing. Then, about midday on the Saturday they decided to head back down to Byrock to be there in plenty of time. The only trouble was, when they got to Byrock, there's no railway trucks, no bloody sheep, nothing. So they get on the phone back to Bathurst and they say to the feller in charge, 'Look, we've just arrived out here to pick up a load'a sheep and there's nothing here. What's going on?'

'You silly bastards,' he said, 'that trip was cancelled on Friday.'

So they took the engine all the way out there and then had to bring it all the way back without a load. And Arthur reckoned that, when they got back home they were in huge strife. He said they were docked their pay, they were suspended for a few weeks for buggering around and, of course, the worst of it all was that Arthur reckoned they hardly caught enough fish for a decent bloody feed.

Granville

With the railways, we had some great times, but we also had some rough, heart-breaking times, too. See, I got caught up in the Granville train smash. I wasn't actually in the crash itself, but I was involved as far as my job went. I lived out that way, out west, and I came into work through Granville just an hour or so before it happened. Then later on, the boss came in and said to me, 'You and Jim and three or four others,' he said, 'you'd better get out to Parramatta, quick. We've just had a bad smash and they say that some people have been killed.'

That was the first we'd heard about it. So we jumped into the boss's departmental car and we went straight out to Parramatta railway station. See, Granville's between Parramatta and Central, so they terminate the trains at Parramatta. Anyhow, we were out there all day then, helping out.

And I remember it was strange because there were people sort of just wandering around in a daze and we

had to try and direct them the best we could. And one of
the women, Marge Crook, I worked with her. She was
from the railways office. She was on that Granville train,
coming to work. God, she was so lucky because she
normally sat in one of those carriages that got crushed
but, just on that one morning, she was running a bit late
and the only carriage she could get onto was a carriage
further down the back, so she didn't get caught. But I
saw Marge and she was wandering about in shock and
she had this woman's purse with her. So I went over and
I said, 'Marge, surely you're not going to work?'

'Yes I am,' she said, 'but I've got this woman's purse
and I don't know what happened to her or where she is.'

So we opened the purse and we found out that the
woman was a member of some club; I don't know, some
golf club up around Katoomba or Lithgow or
somewhere. It was up in the Blue Mountains, anyway,
from where the train had come from. It might've been
Katoomba. But we saw this membership card so we rang
the golf club and told them that we worked for the
railways and we explained about the accident and we
asked if they could contact this lady, if they knew her
phone number or whatever, and that we had her purse
and we didn't know if she'd been killed or what.

I mean, nobody knew the magnitude of the accident at
first. Then the bits and pieces started coming in and it just
didn't seem real somehow; how the loco of the train had
derailed and hit the bridge and then the bridge collapsed
and the concrete slab had crashed down on two of the
carriages and all about the cars that'd came down on top

of it when the bridge went down and the people being dragged out from the squashed train carriages and all the people who were still trapped inside and all the dead people and that poor, poor little girl who had to have her arm amputated, just so they could cut her free from the wreck. It just didn't seem real, somehow. It was like you were playing a part in some sort of horror film. But we weren't because we heard how the medics and the police and all the people were helping out. They worked on through the night and in the end something like eighty-three people had been killed and there was over two hundred injured. Oh, God, it was a hell of a mess.

So as far as my time with the railways goes, that was definitely the worst thing that happened while I was there and I guess if you're working for the railways you sort of feel responsible in some odd sort of way when something like that happens. But I mean, it could've happened to any one of us. We all got up and went to work that morning, like we always did. As I said, I'd even come down that same line an hour or so before the accident, and Marge was just lucky that she'd been a couple of minutes late in catching the train on that particular morning. But it just seemed so unfair that those poor, poor people had simply happened to get on the wrong train at the wrong time and were sitting in the wrong carriages.

It's weird when you think about it, isn't it? It just makes you feel so helpless, like you haven't got any control over anything in your own life. But, no, I couldn't sleep for weeks after that, after 18 January 1977, and it still gets to me from time to time. I see their faces. And I'm sure that I'm not the only one. But call it fate, call it bad luck, call it whatever you like, but it was one of those events that certainly changed my outlook on life. I really started to appreciate the things I had … you know, like the wife and kids, and that. Things improved a lot after that.

Gympie the Railway Cop

Not too many people might know about this, although, every now and then I meet someone who can recall this particular railway cop from Gympie, in south-eastern Queensland. I'm even sure there was a country and western song about him called 'Gympie the Railway Cop', and during the Depression and the war years, this Gympie the Railway Cop became one of the most feared and hated railway cops throughout Queensland. Oh, he was a tough, hard, vicious man, especially on those who were hard up and didn't have the money to pay for a train ticket so they'd have to jump the trains, or 'rattlers' as they were called, because that's what they did—just rattle along; the trains, that is, not the blokes that were hard up.

Anyhow, Gympie the Railway Cop, he happened to have one hand missing and in its place they'd put a big hook. Now, what a lot of the fellers used to do was, when they jumped a rattler, if they couldn't get into one of the enclosed wagons, they'd hide under the railway tarpaulins that were covering the open, flat-top wagons. Of course, when that happened, sometimes your head could be seen bulging from under the tarp, and this Gympie the Railway Cop, he'd sneak up on you, real quiet like, and he'd smash you on the head with his hook. Yeah, *Crack!* Then if he heard anyone talking in one of the enclosed wagons, he'd tap on its sliding door and call out in a down-and-out voice, 'Any room for one more? Any room for one more?' Then as soon as you opened the door, he'd arrest you all.

Anyhow, there was this train called the Sunshine Milk Train. It got that name because it went from Brisbane up as far as the township of Gympie, picking up milk along the way, before it returned back to Brisbane. Gympie the Railway Cop was so much hated that, one time, some hobos jumped him and they tied him up on the railway line, just under a pedestrian bridge. And they tied him there, in that exact spot, because it was right on a bend where the train driver wouldn't be able to see him until it was too late. So they really wanted to kill him, eh.

Then at about two o'clock in the morning a sixteen-year-old girl was walking across the bridge on her way home. It was just before the Sunshine Milk Train was due through and she heard Gympie the Railway Cop crying out, 'Help. Help.' So she climbed down the embankment and she untied him. So she saved his life, eh. And do you know what he did in return? He arrested that girl for trespassing on railway property. Yeah, that's true. So he was a railway cop in the strictest terms of the word, right down to the marrow of his bones, eh.

But, of course, a lot of those railway fellers weren't anywhere near as bad as that. I remember one night, we weren't much more than kids really, and a few of us were in Roma and we wanted to go out to Charleville, where we'd heard there was work on the cattle properties out that way. We didn't have any money so of course we decided to jump a rattler. The trouble being, there was only one enclosed wagon and that was right up next to the engine, where we'd be easily seen. So the next best thing was to go further down the train and climb up under the tarp covering a flat wagon, which happened to be carrying bore castings.

Anyhow, we jumped aboard with our saddles and swags and we made ourselves as comfortable as we could under the tarp, in amongst all these bore castings. But we didn't get very far before the train started shunting our little wagon around. Then, when things had quietened down a bit, I had a look around and there we were, we'd been shunted all by ourself, off onto a little side track.

'This's no good,' we thought, so we grabbed our gear and we raced along to where the guard's van was. See, back then, when they were transporting livestock, they had a van thing for the guard plus they had another little sleeping box, for what was called the train drover, and in between the van and the box, they could put twenty or thirty head of cattle. So we just jumped into the box-part where the train drover camped. Anyway, the guard came along with a hurricane lamp and he spied us. And this guard feller, he knew me because I used to jump the old rattler out along that line quite often. So when this guard saw me, he said, 'Goldsmith, what're you and yer mates up to?'

'Oh,' I said, 'we heard there's work out at Charleville.'

Anyway, he said, 'Well, this train won't take you all the way out to Charleville. But,' he said, 'there's another one coming along soon so just hang around a bit and I'll see if I can sneak you on that one.'

So he was one of the railway fellers who wasn't too bad, eh.

Honesty

If the change from steam to diesel signalled the end of the 'good old days' of the railways then, when David Hill became the Minister of Transport in New South Wales, well, you could just about hear the nails being hammered into the coffin. Right away, with all his economic rationalism and stuff, us technical staff were taken off the trains. That's why they didn't last long. They weren't maintained properly and so they just became a nightmare.

So we were moved out of our home base at Eveleigh and crashed into all these other jobs. I came under the Electric Train Running section and was called 'equipment examiner'. But the only job I could get as an equipment examiner was out at Hornsby, which meant that if I was on the early shift I was up at God knows what hour to get out there to start work, and if I was on the late shift I was left without transport home. On top of that, with us coming into these new jobs there was a lot of resentment from many quarters, which resulted in us receiving quite a few put-downs, and we weren't exactly that stupid, or so I thought.

Anyhow, perhaps I was over-trying because it was one of my first jobs at Hornsby. Well, you think you're doing the right thing but I broke all the rules and regulations, as simple as that. Anyhow, I started at 5 am. Next thing, the phone rings. It's the controller. 'Listen,' he says, 'there's a 5.32 coming out of Hornsby yard. It has to meet the train to Berowra. The main compressor's gone on one car and the main generator's gone on another.'

At that stage, I hadn't worked out the movements of the electric trains. 'Okay,' I thought, 'it must be coming out of Hornsby yard, into the station, then going up to Berowra.' So I'm looking around and there's one of the old red rattlers. 'There's my train,' I think. Now, the procedure is, you're supposed to tell the driver what you're doing because the brakes were supposed to be put in full emergency. But I thought, 'Well, I needn't go up and see the driver because he knows what's wrong and he'll be down soon to see me. It'll save some time.'

Anyway, I get my tools out, put them up on the floor of the train. I lower the pantograph and I just pull the bloody fuse out when I hear this *pssss*. It's the brakes. Then the train starts to move. Next thing I'm watching these two cherry-red tail-lights disappear down the main north line. 'Well,' I thought, 'they must be going on the triangle to bring it back to Platform Four.'

Anyway, I wait, but no train. So I go and see the station bloke. 'Yes,' he says, 'that particular train does go to Berowra alright, but first it goes to Penrith, via North Sydney, before it comes back up to Berowra.'

Shit. So I get on the phone to the controller and I say, 'Do you want the good news or the bad news?'

Well, he went right off the air. 'What do you fuckin' want me to do about it?' he shouted.

'Look,' I said, 'all my tools are laid out on the floor, so when it goes through Central railway station, could you get one of the fellers there to grab them and I'll collect them later.'

Anyway, about half an hour later he rings back. 'I hope yer fuckin' satisfied,' he says.

'What's up?'

'Well,' he said, 'that train just got slower and slower, didn't it, because the end power car's not working. So,' he said, 'the driver got out at Chatswood.' I mean, Chatswood of all places. That's one of Sydney's main stations. Then he says, 'Well, the driver went down to see what was wrong with his train and he saw the pantograph down. So he went to put it back up and there's all the equipment examiner's tools on the floor and it's all too much for him, he collapses, and now we've had to take him away in an ambulance.'

'Oh dear,' I said.

'So,' he said, 'you've shut the whole fuckin' system down and right in the middle of bloody peak hour.'

Anyway, I left him to it and after my shift I went down to Central and I was telling some mates about what'd happened and they're saying, 'Look, yer gotta tell them this. You gotta tell them that.' All the excuses in the world, see.

And I said, 'No I won't, I'll just tell them the truth.'

'You'll get the bloody sack,' they said.

'Well,' I said, 'I'll just have to buy the newspaper on Saturday then, won't I, and look for another job.'

So next day, the phone goes and a bloke introduces himself as the Engineer-in-Charge of Electric Train Running. 'You did a job for us yesterday,' he says.

I said, 'Hang on, I'll just get my diary out.' See, I was still wanting to play poker. Then I said, 'Yes, that was me.'

'Well, what when wrong?' he asked.

'To be honest,' I said, 'I completely fucked it up.'

So I told him what'd happened and he said, 'Look, I've got to answer to the Minister for Transport over this and the shit'll hit the fan with all the media because you shut the whole system down in peak hour.'

'Well,' I said, 'I don't expect you to tell lies on my behalf. In hindsight,' I said, 'I wish I could rub it all out, but I really thought I was saving time. I misunderstood my instructions. It's my fault, nobody else's.'

'Do you know what?' he said. 'God, it's refreshing to talk to someone around here who's honest and frank. Look,' he said, 'just leave it to me. I'll sort the minister out but, for God's sake, don't do it again, will you.'

I said, 'No, I won't. Look, I do apologise.'

So on the way home I called into Central to go to the pub with the boys and I told them how the bloke'd rang up and I'd told him exactly what'd happened.

'Oh, you're gone then,' they reckoned. 'You'll get the bloody sack for sure.'

'Well, if I'm gone,' I said, 'at least I'll go with my integrity.'

And do you know what? I never heard another thing about it. I mean, you couldn't have made a bigger mistake because I totally annihilated the metropolitan service during peak hour. And I thought just how lucky I was, you know, that the railways still had a little of its soul left. Yes, and just because I was honest.

I'll Walk Beside You

I've got three railway stories for you, okay, and they're all about slow trains. The first one came from old Bill Scott, an old droving mate of mine, and it was written up in the Stockman's Hall of Fame magazine, one time. I forget when. Now, knowing Bill, I don't know if this one's true or not but it went something like this. Do you know that song 'I'll Walk Beside You'? Well, that phrase was often used, in the south-west of Queensland, concerning the Barcaldine to Aramac train.

This train was owned, I believe, by the Aramac Shire Council. It opened in 1911 and ceased operating in 1975. But during the 1950s Bill was a guard, employed by the Queensland Railways, and on one occasion he relieved the Aramac guard for a fortnight while he went on holidays. Now, twice a week the train left Aramac at five in the morning and arrived in Barcaldine, which was 42 miles away, at three in the afternoon, and that's only if everything went to schedule. So it took ten hours to go 42 miles, meaning that it only travelled at about 4 miles an hour.

Anyhow, as the story goes, one morning, the train was on its way to Barcaldine and it came across a swaggie who was packing up his gear, ready to move on. So the train driver pulled up and said, 'Do yer want a lift?'

And the swaggie replied, 'No thanks, mate, I'm in too much of a hurry.'

So that's old Bill's story. Another one goes that the driver of that same train—the Aramac to Barcaldine train—could throw a handful of daisy seeds out from the engine and by the time the guard's van came past the seeds had germinated so much that the guard could pick the daisy flowers. Of course, seeing that the train was only about two or three carriages long, that story's definitely not true. It's only a throw-off at the slowness of the train.

Then another incident that happened with the Aramac to Barcaldine train—and this is true—was that it was a good few hours late one day and the stationmaster was concerned so he sent out a navvy crew to see what had happened. Anyhow, about 25 mile out from Barcaldine they'd had a massive downpour and, being that black soil, the train line had actually sunk a foot into the ground and they discovered that train was completely bogged. So then they had to wait for three or four days until the ground dried out before they could get the train moving again. But the funny thing was—and this is definitely true—on that occasion they didn't get a spot of rain at either Barcaldine or Aramac—not one spot—it only rained in that one particular area.

Now, the last story is also true because I was there. A steam train called the Forty-Two Up used to leave

Cloncurry—that's up in north-western Queensland—on a Saturday night at around 10 pm and head for Townsville, over on the coast. I don't know why it was called the Forty-Two Up. It might've been just a codename. Anyhow, it had two passenger carriages and it had a mixed goods van as well. Now this train had a reputation in as much as it'd never been known to arrive on time—not to my knowledge, anyway. In fact, it wasn't uncommon for the thing to arrive anywhere up to eight hours late. Fair dinkum, eight hours late. And the main reason was, that this Forty-Two Up would stop at every blessed fettler's camp along the way and the driver and the fireman and the guard, they'd all get out and wander over to have a yarn with the fettlers' wives and have a cup of tea with them and so forth and so on. Then, when all that was done, they'd wander back to the train and get on their way again until they reached the next fettlers' camp.

Anyway, one time, me and a mate was on this Forty-Two Up. We were around all those little one-horse-pub towns like Nelia and Nonda, between Julia Creek and Charters Towers, where there's not much to occupy your time. All you see out the train window is big mobs of mimosa. Mimosa's a short bush. You wouldn't get one much over 10 feet, but it had savage thorns on it. Anyhow, we were going that slow that I could just about count the thorns on these mimosa bushes as they meandered by the window.

By this stage, I'm just sitting there, mesmerised by this mimosa. Then, I couldn't believe my eyes but, blow me down, the train started to pick up a bit of pace. 'This's odd,' I said to me mate. But it didn't just stop there. The old Forty-Two Up continued to pick up speed until we were really rattling along.

'Beauty,' I said to me mate, 'it's gonna make up for lost time.'

Then, just as we began to really hoot along, suddenly, the train come to a screeching halt. 'Goldie,' me mate said, 'maybe they just forgot where the brakes were fer a while.'

Anyhow, I looked out the window to see what the trouble was and here's the fireman and the driver walking back along the track and one of them had a rifle in his hands.

'Geez,' I said, 'this's odd.'

So me mate come over and we stuck our heads out the window and we seen them walk over to a dead dingo and they got out a knife and they started to scalp the thing. So that explained why the train had been going so fast, eh. They were chasing this dingo, and they had their rifles up the front, in the cabin there, and they shot the thing. Of course, back in them days there was a bounty on a dingo of about a pound, and sometimes the cocky— the property owner—would give them five pounds. But, blow me down, there I was thinking they were making up for lost time.

So anyway, all us passengers, we just sat around in the train waiting until they scalped this dingo and hung its carcass on the fence. Then when we finally got under way again, I drifted back into counting the thorns on the mimosa bushes as they passed by.

It's a Fact

I tell you, things were tough back then. That's how it was for everybody. You learnt the hard way. But here's one story for you. In the Depression years they were re-laying some of the railway lines, cutting through the north of the town. There was about thirty fettlers working in the gang, all with picks and shovels, and so forth and so on, and there was this head ganger. And by God, this head joker was tough. All he done was, he stood over these fettlers all day long, shouting orders and checking his pocket watch, which was hanging on a chain out of his waistcoat, and he'd wait for the big hand to hit the knock-off time or the smoko time before he'd let them take their break or knock off.

Any rate, they had a waterbag hanging up under a big canvas coverage—a shadecloth sort of thing—and one stinking hot summer's day this fettler feller by the name of Alf was thirsty and he decided to walk down to where they had the waterbag. Any rate, with all the heat and things, this Alf wasn't feeling too good so he had a drink and when he was coming back another fettler mate of his, a chap called Tom, said, 'Geez, Alf, you don't look too good, you'd better come back with me and get another drink.' Which he did.

Then after Tom and Alf had their drink they were both heading back to start work again and this head ganger joker, he come over and he said to Alf, 'Yer sacked, Alf.'

'Why?' asked Alf.

'Fer wasting bloody time, that's why,' the head joker said.

So poor old bloody Alf, he got the sack for having a drink of water when it was hot and he was feeling crook. And, of course, in them times, being sacked from the government meant that you never got another job with them afterwards. That's unless you changed your name, of course, and any amount of them did that.

Any rate, that's what this Alf done. After the war years, he changed his name and he got a job back as a fettler. And that was a laugh, you see, because everybody knew he'd got the sack before the war. Any rate, so then he was a fettler for a while and he then become a head ganger, himself, and he stayed that way until he retired.

So there you go. That's how tough it was in them days. It's not like today. I say, today, I don't know how the hell the economy can keep going at the rate it's going, at the present time. The point is, everything you produce you're getting less for. I had a letter here from in the *Stock Journal*. I knew the joker that wrote it. It was about the price of superphosphate. He said the dollar's up but all the imports like super, where it should be down, it's gone up. And it's our leaders what are doing that. Oh, yes. It's a fact. I mean, just how much longer we can continue to live in a fool's paradise, I don't know. She's got to come to an end one day. I always say to young people, if you talk to an old bloke, it's surprising what you'll learn in five minutes. That's true. But if they're not prepared to listen, then you're not prepared to tell them anything, are you, eh. Oh yes, they've got all these bloody degrees and things, alright, but they don't know a thing. Most of them are 'university-educated idiots', as I call them. That's all they are. They see a lot in books but they've got no practical experience whatsoever.

There was a kid here recently, an accountant's son, and he wanted me to teach him how to kill a sheep. See what I mean? He was supposed to be taught how to kill a sheep in some schoolbook or other. But you can't learn just out of books. You've got to have people with practical experience to train these young people, to show them how it's done.

Any rate, I reckon that's what's wrong with society today. She's a complicated turnout, I can tell you.

Jinx

My name's Reg Hart. I was born in 1915, at Charleville, in western Queensland, and that was where I had my first train travelling experience. Mind you, this's back in the early 1920s when the first motor cars were making an appearance out that way, so a train was still the usual means of long-distance travel.

We had what we called the 'Puffing Billy', which was really a Class C17-type loco. We just gave it that name because of the amount of smoke and coal dust it puffed out on its way along the tracks when we went visiting or during the rugby league football season, when it carried players and supporters to nearby towns.

Then, during the Great Depression, I remember how the swagmen would jump the rattler when they went from one place to another in search of work. And when the train slowed on its approach to town, it was a real sight to see all these swaggies jumping from all parts of the train and running off to try and evade the rail fare. Of course, most of the engine drivers and guards, they turned a blind eye to that sort of thing because they were extremely sympathetic towards the unemployed. Well, they were very hard times. But the Depression years were tough for many. In Charleville, as in other towns, the married people were issued with a chit, which was a piece of paper, that entitled them to groceries. I well recall, as kids we had many a meal of bread and dripping, sprinkled with salt and pepper. Still, it didn't do me too much harm, and a few of my old schoolmates are still around and kicking as well.

And I also recall the time when I was about eighteen and I needed to go out to Mt Isa. It was 1933 and I had to link up with a drover at Camooweal before going into the Northern Territory to bring back a mob of cattle to a station property not far from Charleville. Money was short for me at that point in time, so I went to the local Clerk of Petty Sessions and asked them if they could help.

'That's fine,' the bloke said and I was issued with a chit that entitled me to a seat on the train from Charleville via Brisbane to Townsville, then west to Mt Isa. It also allowed me one meal per day during the period of the train journey. I referred to it as my 'starving stock ticket' because it was such a great help in my own particular time of need. Also, it showed that there was a huge trust in me to repay the money when I returned to Charleville, which I did. Then, from that time on, up until 1942, I was a regular train passenger from Charleville to Mt Isa on my way to Camooweal to do my droving trips. My wife and I have also continued to use the train three or four times a year and we've found that, each time we visit the club car for a meal or a drink, the conversation becomes easier. So, over the years, we've met many interesting people, from all different walks of life.

Oh, that's right—talking about meeting people from different walks of life, I did have an incident on one train journey. See, since 1946, the wife and I have been living in Brisbane and each May we travel out to Charleville to attend the local show and race meeting and catch up with old friends. But, up here in wintertime, a lot of tourists also travel out that way by train, so we sometimes miss out on a first class double sleeping birth and we have to take separate sleeping berths instead. When that happens, we have to settle for an economy sleeper, which means that my wife has to share a cabin with two other ladies while I do the same with two males.

Anyway, on one such trip, I'd settled in my economy sleeper berth and was waiting for the train to depart Brisbane, when two men appeared at the door. Then the tall, larger man said to the other one, 'Go 'n' sit by the window 'n' behave yerself.'

Of course, I was a bit shocked by the tall man's sharp manner, but I let it be. Then while he was complaining about the lack of space for their luggage, the other man stood up and tried to adjust the air-conditioning. 'I told yer ta sit down 'n' behave,' the tall man snapped.

Anyway, the tall man must've seen that I was taken aback by his rough manner because he then explained that he was a prison Correctional Officer and he was escorting the other person—a prisoner—out to the prison camp at Charleville. The next thing he said to the prisoner was, 'I have ta take this luggage down the back so yer'll have ta come along with me.'

So they left. Of course, I was quite worried about having to spend the night in a three-berth cabin with these men. What's more, I was unsure of what type of prisoner the prisoner was. For all I knew he could've been anything from a petty crook to a mass murderer. So I took my jacket, wallet and my watch down to my wife's sleeping cabin and asked her to look after them overnight, just in case. Then later on, when the two men returned, I had the lower berth while the prisoner had the top berth and the officer had the middle berth. And I can assure you, I had a very uneasy sleep on that particular trip.

But I'm afraid that whenever I travel by train I do tend to have some odd misfortune or other. Like, one time, the air-conditioning failed and we were off-loaded onto a bus to finish our journey. Another time there was a train derailment and we had to be bussed to bypass the accident. Then there was the time we were delayed in Sydney when the dining car staff held a strike meeting. There's also been numerous breakdowns, such as the brake locking on the carriages and so forth. Another instance we arrived at Roma and the relief driver couldn't be found so we had to hang around until they'd sorted all that out.

So yes, I have felt that, at times, I'm a jinx to the railways. But then I proved that wrong the time I decided to fly up to Mt Isa instead of going by train, and I somehow managed to get on the wrong plane and I ended up in Darwin by mistake. Oh dear, that was a shemozzle, that was. So nowadays, being my age, if ever I fly anywhere I always ask for a wheelchair, which has helped solve my problem of getting the wrong flight.

But no, train has always been the preferred means of travel for both my wife and myself. We've been all over: from Brisbane to Melbourne, from Sydney to Perth via Adelaide, Brisbane to Cairns, Brisbane to Mt Isa, Brisbane to Longreach, Brisbane to Charleville, many times over. So I hope that some of this information may be of use to you.

Not bad for a man of near on ninety, eh?

Just Magic

Yeah, well, I first started in the railways in 1948 at a place called Stanley, in the far north-west of Tasmania. I was eighteen years old and began as an engine cleaner, then I went on the track as a fireman. They had one engine there, at Stanley, and every day it used to take about three hours to get the steam up, then we'd head out, about 20 miles south, to a place called Trowutta and deliver down there. See, back in them days, everything was carted by rail: all the beer, everything, groceries, the works.

Then I was transferred to Wynyard and we did Wynyard to Launceston on a passenger train. And that first trip as a fireman bloody near killed me. Geez, it knocked me about. You've got no seat so you have to stand for about six hours and, when they hit the corners, your bloody hip hits the side of the engine. Then bang, you're over the other side. So it was pretty hard yakka being a fireman, but I loved it in the finish. I didn't get to be a driver. You had to be there fifteen years or something to be a driver, I think. But the drivers I worked with were real old gentlemen, most of them. They were all characters.

I remember one bloke, a driver by the name of old Bong Wills. Bong was his nickname. This's around 1949 or 1952. See, there was a railway terminal in the midlands, there at Parattah, just out of Oaklands. Anyhow, we were coming up from Hobart, one night. It's about 52 miles. It's uphill all the way and this Bong Wills, he was about fifty-five. Well, that night Tassie had the biggest snowstorm in history and when we pulled up at a place called Campania, old Bong said to me, 'Geez, if we get stuck in this snow, we'll perish. Can you can keep the coal up to her? I'll have to hurry her up or we'll be goners.'

Well, that got me a bit worried so I said, 'Okay.'

Anyhow, he hurried her up alright. We had 200 ton on behind us and I was so scared that we'd get snowed in and we'd die that I shovelled like I'd never shovelled in me life, either before or since. God, he had me working. Anyhow, we arrived in Parattah about three-quarters of an hour ahead of time and I was telling another bloke at the station about how Bong reckoned we'd die in the snow if we didn't get a hurry-on and the bloke said, 'Nah, that's all bull.' He said, 'Bong's got a new girlfriend and he just wanted to get home early to go to bed with her.'

Then there's another thing that happened on that same line. I suppose I shouldn't repeat it but the poor buggers are dead now, anyway. One Saturday evening, I was on me own. It was raining. I had me singlet on. I'd just got out of the shower and I was having some tea when I heard this God-awful crash. So I went outside and the driver had backed the train straight through the end of the engine shed. Straight through. So I walked up and I said, 'Hey, yer've stuck the van through the shed.' Then I seen that the driver and the fireman, they were both drunk. They were so bad that they had a job to stand up. I should've reported it, I know, but being a kid you don't bother, do you?

Anyhow, so I just went back and I finished me tea and I went to bed. But when they left, they absolutely roared out of the station, then they turned her over down the bottom of the tunnel hill. The engine went over one way and the train went over the other way, into the gully. They reckoned they was doing 80 mph around the corner when she left the tracks. Lucky it didn't kill them, eh. Then when they pulled the engine back up on the rails there wasn't a mark on it. Even today, I still feel bad about not reporting them. But I was only a kid and, see, even if I did, they would've gone out that night, anyway.

Then there was another time I'll never forget. It was when I first started firing with the railways and we used to take the workers' train to Boyer. Boyer's a paper mill place near New Norfolk. So we'd go to New Norfolk and then wait for an hour and a half before we took the passenger train back to Hobart.

Anyhow, this old driver, he says, 'I'll have some breakfast.'

So I cleaned the fire down for him and he opened the door and he slid in a couple of strips of bacon and some toast and a couple of eggs, then he settled in to watch it cook while I went on cleaning the engine. Anyhow, I seen a bit of dust so I jumped back up to the cabin and I turned on the blower. Now, I just forgot about it but, when you pull the blower, it forces the air into the firebox and up the funnel. So there he was, this old driver, sitting there looking at his breakfast cook and all of a sudden— *Zoop!*—it disappeared straight up the funnel, right before his very eyes.

'Christ,' he said. 'Me bloody breakfast, it's gone.' Then he took one look at me and he grabbed the hammer and he said, 'I'll git you, you little bastard.'

So I took off and he chased me up the road. Gawd, I thought he was going to kill me. Oh, I'll never forget that.

Anyhow, after a bit, he started laughing. 'Bugger it,' he said. 'I'll have to go and buy a bloody pie now.'

Then there was another time—this was back when I was a young engine cleaner at Stanley and they bought what they called a Garratt locomotive. The Garratt was about 150 ton. It had four pistons, two each end, and the cab was in the middle of the cylinders. And I was a bit of a bugger with the locomotives, see, because when I used to get their steam up, I'd race them up and down the line at about one or two o'clock in the morning, for a bit of a thrill drive, like.

Now the drivers must've known I was doing this so when this new Garratt came in, one particular driver came over and he said, 'Don't touch this Garratt.'

'Why's that?' I said.

He said, 'Just don't touch it.'

So I said, 'Right, okay.'

Anyhow, underneath each cylinder of the Garratt locomotive there's a steam cock. You opened it and it let the condensed steam out of the cylinder. But the thing is, if it's shut, the water won't compress and you open the throttle and it blows water into the cylinder. You see, that was the danger of it. Anyhow, I said, 'Bugger him.'

So I had 180 pound pressure on and I pulled the throttle and all the water spewed out, then steam started coming out and I shut it off and she started to move, you see.

'This's pretty good,' I said. So I let her go. The next thing—*bang!*—there's this almighty bloody explosion. It frightened the hell out of me. So I jumped down off the engine and looked around, but no, I couldn't see any damage.

'This's no good,' I said.

Then I thought I'd better get the Garratt back in the shed before anybody found out that I'd taken it out. But just as I'm putting it back into the shed—*Bang!*—there's another bloody awful explosion. So then I look around and I see the driver coming down and he didn't look too happy. 'Gawd, I'm done for now,' I thought.

'Didn't I bloody well tell you not to move that Garratt?' he said.

What could I say, I'd been caught red-handed, so I said, 'What's happened?'

'Well,' he said, 'I knew you wouldn't be able to resist taking it out so I put detonators on the rails to scare the Christ out of you.'

So he caught me out, and he certainly frightened the Christ out of me, alright. But oh, I enjoyed the old steam. There was sort of something magic about it, really. You'd get up in the morning, put the fire and things on and it'd take about an hour for the water to boil and when it got to boil you'd see the steam hand creeping up. Then you'd pull a lever and the bloody thing would start to move. It was just magic. You didn't have to turn on a motor or anything. They were just incredible machines.

Kurdaitcha Man

Many, many years ago, when I was working for the ABC, I went for a run up to 5CK, Port Pirie, with John Starr, the chief engineer, where we meet up with Bert Rowe. Bert was the original manager of 5CK. He was an accountant really, so he didn't know too much about broadcasting, which caused his boss to describe him, very affectionately, as being 'a terrific chap, salt of the earth, but a card of a broadcaster'. See, they couldn't get people to go out bush back in those days and Bert was game, so he got the job.

Anyway, from Pirie, we all decided to drive towards the West Australian border to check on our radio coverage in that area. We had a four-wheel drive Land Rover so we went out through places like Kyancutta, Poochera, Nunjikompita, through Ceduna. Then just past Fowlers Bay we cut up north to the little settlement of Ooldea before we started to drive back in an easterly direction on the maintenance track that ran beside the east–west railway line. The trouble was that this track was very rough because it'd been gouged out of the red sandy soil and the configuration of it made it seem like we were riding huge stationary waves. It went up and down, up and down, with about 100 to 200 yards between each crest. The railway line had been cut through these sand dunes and so, as you came to the top of these peaks, you'd find yourself looking down on the track.

I was driving at the time and, to get over these sandhills I had to take a fair run at them. Then as I got near the top, I had to slow down because I couldn't see if anyone was coming towards us in the opposite direction. So that's what I was doing, going flat out up the crest, then slowing down near the peak and hoping the momentum would carry us safely over the top. But then, on one of these peaks, I slowed down a bit too much and the Land Rover sank down to its axles in all this red sand and we got well and truly bogged.

Now, all along the railway line there were these little sidings where the fettlers would live in a small community and they'd look after 50 miles or so of track. So it was decided that we'd head to one of these for help. To that end we tossed a coin to determine which way we'd go. Heads it was, and so then we set out, east again, along the railway line to get help. It was about two o'clock in the afternoon and John was a bit short of hair so he took along his umbrella.

Anyhow, we'd been going for several hours and by that stage it was dark, and out there, under all those stars it's so quiet you can hear the silence. Then out from that silence we heard the sound of a train coming from, probably, 20 or 30 miles away. And as the train approached, with all its lights shining, John stepped out onto the middle of the track and started waving his umbrella for the train to stop.

Now, I've often wondered just what might've gone through the train driver's mind at that moment. Here he was, no doubt he'd been driving for hours out in the middle of the Nullarbor Plain, in the middle of the night, and the only living thing he'd probably seen was the odd kangaroo or two and suddenly, out of nowhere, he sees, or he thinks he sees, a white balding bloke waving an umbrella at him. I mean, you'd wonder about your sanity wouldn't you—which I presume he did for a brief moment because, just as John dived off the track the brakes came on and sparks were flying every bloody place. But then the driver must've decided that it was all just an apparition because he took the brakes off and we watched as his 'tail-lights' disappeared into the distance.

So we picked John up, dusted him off and we kept on walking until we eventually reached a little siding. I forget what the place was called but there were only four or five houses and about three of them had their lights on. We could hear people talking inside the first house so we started banging on the door. But all of a sudden there was complete silence. We knocked again but still nobody replied. So we called out, 'We know you're in there. Can you answer the door, please.' But not a soul.

We thought that this was a bit odd so we went over to the next house. Knock … knock. And we kept knocking until the lights went out and an Aboriginal voice shouted, 'Go away, you're at the wrong house.' Then dead quiet.

By now we're thinking that this is the most inhospitable place you're ever likely to come across. Anyhow, like the three little pigs we moved on to the third house and, thankfully, this time someone answered the door. It turned out to be the head ganger, an Australian bloke, and didn't he have a good laugh when we told him we'd been banging on doors and nobody would answer them.

'They're Abos,' he said. 'You've scared the shit out of them because they think you're the Kurdaitcha Man.'

Now, to the Aborigines, the Kurdaitcha Man is the magic man, the fella who has the mystical powers to point the bone and kill people if they'd done anything wrong. So all these Aborigines must've thought that they'd done plenty wrong and we'd appeared out of the darkness to come and hex them or something.

Anyway, the head ganger sorted it out and they ended up being very good to us. They got out one of those track-maintenance trikes and we all clambered onto that to head back to our Land Rover. But our troubles weren't quite over yet because further along the track we had to branch off the main line because a train was coming. So one of the blokes got down and changed the points system on the rail line. The only trouble was, it was still dark and the head ganger couldn't see where the end of the side track was and, when we reached it, he kept on going and we were catapulted into the air. Trike and all was scattered all over the place.

But apart from a few bruises and things, none of us were seriously hurt so when the train had passed we managed to get the trike out back onto the main line and we eventually reached our Land Rover. It was early morning by then and all these Aboriginal fettlers helped us out of the bog and then we drove off, back towards civilisation. This time, we didn't bother to slow down when we neared the top of the sandhills. We just ripped over the lot of them, flat out.

Last Train Out

Well, my father was originally on the Meekatharra mines, in the mid-west of Western Australia. Then after the mines shut down he worked in the restaurant at the railway station for a while before they got him a job in Perenjori, as a navvy—a labourer—on the Mullewa to Perth line. So he was working on the Mullewa to Perth track there, for a couple of years, living in tents. That was round about 1936.

Then when they put the line in from Mt Magnet, east to Sandstone, they said he'd be promoted to a ganger if he went up there. So he did that, but it must've been pretty tough work because he once told me how they started one morning with twenty men and by lunchtime there was only six left. Oh, they had to load the ballast into the rail trucks by wheelbarrow and all that. You know, wheel it up the plank, and it knocked them all up. Then when he finished there he was transferred to Tuckanarra before he got a job back along the Mullewa line as a boss, and there he stopped.

It's hard to say, but I think he stayed with the railways for thirty years or so.

We lived right alongside the railway line, you know, and, oh, it was a great life for a kid. We'd hop a ride on the train when it first took off from the station and we'd jump off down the other end, after it got going. And when they were shunting around the yards we'd always go over and have a ride in the engine. Of course, it was all on the quiet, because they wouldn't have been allowed to carry kids about like that. Also the crews would chuck a bit of coal off the tender so we could use it in our house fires, you know. And being the ganger, Dad used to run the length each day to see if things were alright. He did that in a little trike that ran up and down the line. But if that broke down he'd drive the truck and us kids'd cop a ride with him.

In a lot of those little towns along that line there were only about seven or ten men working in the gang and that was just enough to keep a place alive, perhaps with a little school. We didn't live in big houses. They only had little rooms, but they were good houses. And there was a 400-gallon tank alongside the railway line for each house, and in summer a special train would come through and they'd siphon water out of the railway tanks, into the 400-gallon tanks, for all of us to use.

But everything was carted by steam train back then. Passenger trains came through three times a week, one up, one back, to Mullewa, and all the freight come up by train. That went right through to Meekatharra. Oh, there was a road but it was pretty rough. Stuff didn't come by road. It all came by train, them days. Oh, and another thing, I remember how they'd bring the bread down from Perenjori in those old wooden tea-chests, about 3 foot square, and, one day, they left it on the station and one of the farmer's cows came along and knocked it off and everyone ran out of bread.

And another funny thing I remember was the Ormsley Special. That was the nickname for the train that came up every Saturday morning. Ormsley was the guard and he was always drunk. He got so bad that no-one ever trusted him to get their luggage and stuff off the train. So, when it stopped, people went and got their own gear out of the guard's van or else it'd be over-carried and go further on up the line. Then, at Caron, there used to be a refreshment station and they'd run beer and, one time, this Ormsley got stuck into the grog and the train left without him, so they had to load him into a car and chase the train down.

But over the years it's dwindled off. Most of the kids that were there are sure dead now, and after the steam trains they went into the diesels, then they sort of cut the diesels out. Nowadays there's no passenger trains anymore. It's all buses now. Now the railways only cart wheat—that's all. Then about three weeks ago I was reading in a paper here about how they've just run the last train out from Mullewa to Meekatharra and they're going to pull all the track up. That was more or less the rail out to the old goldfields. I mean, some of that track from Narngulu out to Mullewa, well, that was laid even before the 1900s. So there you go, she's all over now.

Latham

Latham's in a wheat and sheep area, on the railway line, about halfway between Perth and Geraldton, and back in the 1940s, when I was a young girl, there wouldn't have been more than forty people living there. There was just one shop, a wheat bin, a few houses—mainly railway houses—and we had a little school with one teacher and about twenty kids. Our education just went up to Grade Seven and then, if we wanted to further our education, we had to go away to boarding school, mainly to Geraldton.

After my father, Ted Waugh, took over as the ganger, we stayed in Latham until the gang closed in about 1964. Being the ganger, Dad was like the foreman in charge of about eight fettlers, as the workers were called, and they did the repairs along that particular stretch of the railway line. But especially for my mother, some of those times were more unhappy than happy because she came from a farm at Greenough, where she had plenty of water and plenty of food and plenty of everything, more or less. But at Latham there was nothing. I guess others had to do the same, though. Of course, as kids you didn't realise how hard it was. Kids are adaptable. They just get on with it, don't they?

Then after the war, in about 1949 a lot of what were called New Australians came from Europe to work on the rails. They were described as 'displaced people' and, to repay getting their fare out here, they had to give the Australian government two years' service before they could go and work at their own profession. I found them to be really lovely people and they gave us new recipes, so our culinary range improved. But I remember one sad thing. One of the New Australian couples had a little baby and he died. I think it was with the heat, because Latham got very hot in the summertime and they only had corrugated-iron houses and those houses got very, very hot. And I guess, coming from where it's a lot colder, it was too much for the little boy.

Then also, with it being so dry, the railways had to bring in water, and we had to cart it in buckets over to our houses and pour it into the copper or the wash trough or, if we were having a bath, we'd put it in the bath. And, oh, my mother, she was a great gardener. She'd save all the rinse water from the washing and the bath and she'd bail it out onto her geraniums and her few pot plants, to keep them going. Most of the people used to do that. It was amazing what they could get going with the little bit of water we had. Mum also had a lemon tree and—that's right!—Mrs Syson had a lemon tree and a fig tree. And I can remember that Mrs Syson kept a cow tethered in the bush, and she had a bush shed where she did her milking and she'd give her spare milk to everybody. And Mrs Syson, she was also very good with babies because we were a long, long way from a doctor.

But with the New Australians—I remember one time when my sister, Rosalie, was only about three or four and she taught all the foreign children how to make mud pies and, oh, the mothers were so distraught at the terrible mess they got themselves into. And also, Rosalie used to pick up the languages of the other children and she'd come home and Mum wouldn't have a clue what she was talking about. Of course, Rosalie used to teach them English, too. It was amazing how little children so easily caught hold of each other's language.

But dear me, it must've also been so hard for some of those displaced people because most of them weren't used to labouring work. Many were well-educated people, like schoolteachers and so forth. Then having come from those big cities in Europe to arrive in Latham in summer, well, the poor things must've wondered where on earth they'd come to, what with all the heat and the dust and the flies. Then there was no refrigeration or anything like that. And when they first arrived, they didn't even have a waterbag, and I can still see Mum sewing one up for them. So it was very, very hard for them. Though, really, most of us didn't have much apart from a few basic amenities and, of course, everybody helped each other out more, back in those days.

Then this is where I feel a bit sad. After the New Australians had done their two years, most of them went to Perth to take up their professions or whatever. And, after that, in about 1950 most of the men that came to work on the rail were heavy drinkers and there were lots of fights and their children were neglected. So that was unpleasant, and my mother grew quite bitter because of the types we had around us. She reckoned it was all because the government had to find jobs for the people who'd come out of jail. So they sent them to the country, to Latham. That's what my mother said, anyway.

But one funny thing I remember: there were two old Irishmen, Paddy and Tom. Fettlers, they were. I don't think they were out of a jail but they'd go on the square for a few weeks then they'd go on a bender, as they called it. And my father was English, and the English and the Irish weren't very friendly and when old Tom got drunk he used to march up and down the front, past our house, calling Dad a 'black and tan, Pommy so-and-so'.

Then the other fettler, old Paddy, he'd get so drunk that he couldn't walk home. And when that happened, Tom used to load him into a wheelbarrow. And oh, it was funny. I can still see it. As a kid I used to stand out there and watch old Tom trying to wheel old Paddy home in this wheelbarrow. And Paddy was like a dead weight and he'd have his legs dangling out the front, his arms dangling out the side and his head flopping over the back, and Tom'd be drunk as well and the wheelbarrow would be zigzagging all over the street, and they'd topple over and Tom'd stumble about while he tried to lift Paddy back into the wheelbarrow. Then they'd head off again, zigzagging and toppling over all along the way. Oh, sometimes, it used to take them hours to get home.

Lifeline

I think it was around 1956 when we went out on the Transcontinental Line. Mick, my husband, was a fettler. First, we came up from Perth to Parkeston, which is just out of Kalgoorlie. At that point of time, Parkeston, in Western Australia, and Port Augusta, in South Australia, were the main places for the Commonwealth Railways, and they had big stores there where you could do all your shopping.

Then from Parkeston we had to go and stay out at Karonie with my husband's sister because, on the journey up from Perth, they'd lost all our furniture. So we were stranded at Karonie with her for a week, then when they found our furniture, we rejoined the goods train and we went out to Zanthus. And I remember we arrived there at about three in the morning to be greeted by six little houses sitting in the middle of nowhere.

Coming from a big city like Perth, it was a bit of a shock at first. But actually, Zanthus wasn't the most barren or isolated place out along the Nullarbor. There were peppercorn trees along the railway line. There was a small rest house for the crews who were changing trains. The houses were weatherboard, though there was no floor coverings or anything, and we had a thunderbox toilet that had to be taken out bush to be emptied. As for our water supply, every week the Tea and Sugar train brought in water gins or, if we ran out, the goods train would drop one off in the yard. Water gins are those big tankers. We also had very good rainwater tanks, but we only used the rainwater for making tea and that while the brought-in water was used for bathing and cleaning and so forth.

There was also a small, one-teacher school and I remember how the government used to issue the school with liquid Ideal Milk. It wasn't powdered milk. It was an unsweetened milk, in tins, and at ten o'clock each morning the teacher dished that out to the pupils. And because there wasn't a pub, if there was a party or something, the men sent in an order to Kalgoorlie and out would come a huge crate of beer. I can't remember how many bottles a crate held, but each bottle was individually wrapped in straw to protect it. Then some of the special gangs, like at Coonana and places like that, they used to make their own brew. Oh, they were disaster weekends when they got stuck into that. My, oh my, it was powerful stuff.

But when the men went out working of a morning, us women, we'd get together and have a cup of coffee or a cup of tea and a smoke. Those days, I was a smoker. We'd meet at someone's house or just out in the yard. We had big front yards, with a playground. Also, some of the women might get together to sew the children's clothes. Then just before the men knocked off at about four, you'd go home and get a cup of tea ready for them, for as soon as they walked in. Then you'd cook dinner and, being without electricity, it was quite a ritual how, every night, you'd sit down and light up all your Tilley lamps.

For cooking we had a wood stove, and because the Tea and Sugar train came Thursday, I'd always have a big cooking day on Friday. See, each week we'd give our supply order to the ganger who'd ring it through to the railway stores at Parkeston or Port Augusta. And most times too, you know, on the Thursday, before the Tea and Sugar arrived, the women got together and we shared what we had left. Like, somebody might have some flour, another one might have an egg, so we'd make pancakes. Thursday was pancake day.

Oh, and another thing—talking about food—we had a German family that used to go out spotlighting. They were fettlers and sometimes they'd shoot a camel. Anyhow, attached to all our houses was a big long sleep-out, covered in with flywire, and they'd skin this camel and hang it up in the sleep-out. And, oh, the blowflies. I don't know how they found their way in, but you've never seen so many blowflies in all your life. So they'd hang this camel up until it got a greenish film on it, then they'd skin the green film off and cut the animal up and put it in the kerosene fridge.

But the only music we had was a wireless and an old wind-up gramophone. We only had twenty-eight records; Bing Crosby, Louis Armstrong, all those real oldies. I've still got those records but there's not much left in them. Believe me, they're pretty worn out. And on the weekends, all the ladies did a bit of cooking then the families got together and we'd share our food and have a bit of a dance or maybe a singalong if we had musical instruments. One time, I remember we had an Aboriginal family who had a guitar and, oh, they had beautiful voices.

Of course, Cundeelee Mission was just up from Zanthus, and we'd go out there in the back of a truck to visit the people who were running the mission, and go to church. I think it was any denomination, really. It was pretty free and easy anyway, because you'd see the Aboriginal mums sitting in church feeding their babies. And our kids' eyes nearly fell out when they first seen that. It was hilarious. Then you'd see all the Aboriginal people walking about with their spears and that, looking for food.

Then also our schoolkids used to visit the other railway camps for sports days. A train'd bring in a special carriage for us, with water and a kitchen, and we'd go and live in that while the kids did their running and jumps, bike riding and all those sorts of things. The kids really enjoyed it. Father Christmas also came out on the Tea and Sugar train, and the nursing sisters, they'd come out on the Tea and Sugar to check the children over. That Tea and Sugar train, it was a very special train. It stopped at all the sidings across the Nullarbor with our supplies and that. We didn't go without anything. The

Tea and Sugar was our lifeline, really. It was the thing that joined us all together.

And you know, in emergencies, the Commonwealth Railways were very good to us. They always made sure something was done. Like, if a child got sick or if anybody was hurt, I was in charge of the Flying Doctor's outfit and they'd come to me and I'd patch them up until they could catch a train into Kalgoorlie and see the doctor. I didn't have any certificates or anything. I'd been nursing, but that was maternity nursing, actually. One time, the office in Port Augusta rang and asked if I'd join the next goods train coming through because there was a woman on it who was having a miscarriage. So I did, and I accompanied her into Kalgoorlie. She was the wife of one of the fettlers, back down the line. She lost the baby, unfortunately. That was sad. But after she came home she wrote me a very nice note, thanking me for all my help. The people were good like that.

So there you go, we were at Zanthus for two or three years sharing that sort of life with six families and their children.

Lost Loco

My father, Bill Hay, he's in hospital at the moment but he was a well-known train driver up here in Queensland. That was with steam trains, of course, because he's getting on a bit now. But to be the daughter of a train driver, back in those days, was really something, you know. And Dad was so good with us. I remember even before I started school, when we lived in Hughenden, Mum'd take me over to the railway yards and she'd draw a big circle around a telephone pole. 'Megan,' she'd say, 'you sit within that circle until your father comes to get you.'

So I'd sit there, waiting for Dad to come and take me down to the sandpits. You know how they used to drop sand on the tracks to help with the brakes and the traction. They had a big sandpit down there for that, so I'd play in the big sandpit, with the sounds and the smells of the trains all about me. Oh, it was so beautiful. And when I went down to the sandpits, Mum used to make me a couple of arrowroot biscuits with butter on, and this time Dad said to me, 'Don't forget it's good manners to offer my fireman a biscuit.'

So when the fireman came along I said, 'Would you like a biscuit?' And he said, 'Thanks.' And he grabbed one and he ate it and I was so devastated. I just thought it was good manners to offer him a biscuit. In the whole wide world I never thought he'd actually take one, let alone eat it. So the next time I went down I said to Mum, 'You'd better make a couple of extra biscuits because Dad's fireman's a very hungry man.'

Then when we grew up, all the kids at school were so envious about us having a father who drove trains. And me and my sister, we just loved going on trips with Dad out to Wallumbilla. He shouldn't have taken us, of course, but in the morning we'd walk across the paddock from where we lived, near the cemetery, and Dad'd come along and stop the train and we'd climb aboard and go with him. Then, that afternoon, on his way back he'd just let us off and we'd walk home, across the paddock.

The train crews used to stay at Wallumbilla for half an hour or so and, one time, me and my sister, we madly raced around and picked all this wattle and decorated the train engine with it. So there was wattle hanging off everywhere. Oh, we thought it was absolutely fantastic. Then on our way home we were saying to Dad and the fireman, 'Oh, this train's the prettiest train in the whole wide world.'

'Yes, yes, girls, it's beautiful,' they were saying.

Then when Dad let us off, we were walking home across the paddock, thinking how it's going to be the prettiest train ever to arrive at Roma station, then we turn around and we see Dad and the fireman racing around ripping all the beautiful wattle off. Oh, me and my sister were devastated. It was only when I was a few years older that I ever wondered as to just what the station manager would've thought if this train had've chuffed into Roma station, all decorated in wattle. He'd have thought that Dad'd been drinking or something.

But life wasn't all plain sailing. I remember when Dad was one of the two drivers-in-charge of the shifts, at Main Junction in Brisbane, and they lost a train engine. True. See, it was his job to prepare the engines and put them on their different tracks, all ready to go out. Then one day a driver went along to where his train was supposed to be waiting for him, except it wasn't there. So he went back to Dad and he said, 'Where's the loco?' And Dad told him where it was and the driver said, 'No it's not.'

So Dad and the driver went over and the loco had disappeared. 'Strike me roan,' Dad said, or words to that effect.

Then they had a big search but they couldn't find it. Anyhow, Dad and his fellow driver-in-charge were so worried about it all that when anyone from higher up got in touch to find out about what had happened, they'd try and make up some excuse or change the subject real fast. I mean, a steam engine can't just disappear, can it? Everyone knows that, but it did.

Anyhow, this train had been missing for at least a few days when a railway worker wandered across the yards to buy a newspaper and when he arrived back he come over to Dad and he said, 'Bill,' he said, 'I reckon I might've found that lost loco of yours.'

Apparently, what had happened was that when they'd prepared the loco they didn't put the Westinghouse brake on properly and it had just enough steam to chuff off, and it somehow found its own way onto a storing line. Then when the engine ran into those big bumper things at the end of the line, it hit so hard that a weeping willow, right beside it, toppled over and covered it all up. So that was the mystery of the lost loco, solved.

But, oh, he was so good to us kids, Dad was.

Loved It

I was seventeen years old when I went out to live along the Trans-line with my mum, Dad and my two sisters. That was in the late 1930s, early '40s. Dad worked on the line and Mum cooked for the 'mucking out' gangs. Mucking out is cleaning up the mess after they've put the ballast along the railway track. Anyhow, my sister and I, we used to wait on the table and, as I said, Mum did the cooking. There were no shops or anything, so all our supplies came on the Tea and Sugar train that serviced all the little towns and sidings across the Nullarbor.

So that's where I met my husband. Vic was a ganger. He'd come out from Canada by boat but I couldn't say what year because, I mean, as a matter of fact, there was a twenty-year age difference between us and so I never, ever asked about things like that. All I know was, he spent a lot of time travelling around Australia doing different jobs and that he was well known. So I was eighteen when we got married. Then we moved to Woocalla, a little siding on the way to Pimba, in central South Australia. From

there we went back out along the line to Fisher, then over
into Western Australia to Loongana and Zanthus, back
again to Woocalla, then finally, to Port Augusta. So I've
seen a lot of the Nullarbor.

When we first went to Woocalla we lived in an old
blacksmith's quarters while a couple of the single men
were in tents and the other people had decent houses.
There was a little school there. Then when we went to
Fisher we lived in a weatherboard house, I think it was.
But, oh, Fisher was a terrible bad place for those cockeye
bobs. Cockeye bobs are very strong winds that come up
from out of nowhere and whirl like a cyclone and blow
up all this massive dust.

Then at Loongana there was only about a dozen
people. We lived in a weatherboard house there and,
well, I mean, the only time the men really got off was on
the weekends and, more often than not, they'd get a little
10-gallon keg of beer sent down the line and they'd enjoy
themselves that way. They were wooden kegs and they
kept them cold with wet bags or something. Us wives,
we'd also try to make the most of those social times. We
even had a couple of big fancy-dress evenings that were
written up in the *Kalgoorlie Miner*. And I'd polish my
verandah over and we'd play games on that—kids'
games really, but it was fun. Like, there'd be two rows of
men and women, and the men had to pass a ball back
between their legs while the women had to pass it back
over their heads. And one time, this man got in front of
me so I gave him a big shove and he fell straight off the
verandah. Yes, right off.

Another time, the men used to run 'the length' every alternate Saturday. 'The length' is the distance of track that they had to look after and maintain. So they'd run from our camp down to the next camp and then they'd have a few drinks and come back again.

Anyhow, one time, I was waiting for Vic to come home and one of the men came over and asked for some ice-blocks to take over to Vic, and I said, 'No, I'm not going to give him ice-blocks. If he wants ice-blocks he can come and get them himself.' But I didn't know that Vic had fallen over and he'd cracked his head. I felt really sorry about that afterwards. But little incidents like that made life a bit different, and if somebody got really sick they'd have to get on the first train into either Kalgoorlie or Cook. In fact, I had three of my children at the Cook Hospital. It was a good hospital, too.

But out in places like that you get to see things that nobody else would see. Like, at Loongana, in the middle of winter it's absolutely freezing and, one time, we had this east wind, which made it even worse. Anyhow, I'm dressed up in all the warm clothes I've got and across the plains come these three Aboriginals: a man, a woman and a little kid. Well, the woman just had a cotton dress on and the man only wore a loincloth, that's all, and the little kid was stark naked. Oh, I didn't know how they could stand it because it was absolutely freezing. It also gets very, very hot out there. We had a tin shed at the back of our house made into a shower place and in the summer you couldn't bear to stand under it, the water was that hot. And when you came out, your hair stood on end because it was bore water and that's so hard and salty.

But no, never, ever did I feel isolated when I was living out along the Nullarbor. It really was a great life. As a matter of fact, I still go up to Tarcoola every now and again. It's beautiful. My son still lives there. He used to be the stationmaster at Tarcoola. There's no station there anymore, of course, it's virtually a ghost town these days, but he's been interviewed several times over because he knows the place inside out. He knows everything about the old times, the new times and I wouldn't be surprised if he knows about the future, too. But no, it's really a marvellous life out there. I loved it. If I could, I'd pack up today and go back out there and live it all over again.

Lucky Worker Cheats Death

Oh, there's thousands of bloody things from my time in the railways, but I guess the most dramatic was when I hit a rock slide in a section car and they had to get the helicopter out to airlift me to hospital. Well, my position at that stage was track section supervisor, and what happened was, one of the trains had reported a jib swing. Do you know what a jib is? Well, it's sort of like a crane and you pull this jib and it comes down and you fill the steam engines with water.

Anyhow, they asked me if I could have a look at this jib swing on me way out to Normanton. So really, I shouldn't even have been where I was because instead of driving straight out, I put the section car on the track in Cairns and I travelled up the Kuranda Range. There's quite a few tunnels up through there and, anyhow, I just came out of this tunnel—like, from the dark into the daylight—and there's all this dust, bloody everywhere. So I just glanced up the bank to see if I could see anything and when I looked down again I seen that a rock slide had pushed the railway track right over the side and down into the valley.

My first reaction was, 'Oh, bloody hell!' because I just couldn't believe what my eyes were looking at, what with all the bloody line being so smashed up and so forth. But by the time I applied the brakes it was too late, and over I went in this section car and I rolled down the side of the hill about 30 yards. I didn't get knocked out or anything. I was awake all the time, and when I came to a stop I was still in the car and both of us was just in a total mess.

Then I remembered that a train was coming through pretty soon, so I fossicked around but I couldn't find me radio, so I tried to climb out of there, to get up the top and warn the driver. But I couldn't climb up the steep hill. I was all numb because, at that time, I didn't realise about my broken leg—well, not straightaway I didn't, but when it cooled off a bit I certainly did, eh. I'd broken the bone just under the kneecap—the tibia, I think it is—and I'd smashed all just under the cheekbone. Then later on I had about forty bloody stitches in me head and then they found out lots of other things wrong with me as well.

Anyhow, there wasn't anything I could do, so I just lay there listening for this train to come. And it's pretty frightening when you can't do a damn thing. And what you do, of course, is that you start to think the worst, like a derailment or even something worse than that. So I was thinking of all those terrible sorts of things when I heard the train coming through the tunnel.

But just in time, the driver spotted the rock slide and he applied the emergency brakes. So they pulled up just in front of this slide and the guard, he come to have a look over the bank and that's when he seen the section car. Then he came straight down and he took one look at me and they radioed the police and an emergency helicopter, straightaway. And also I was lucky that there was a doctor on the train, because she came down and she stabilised me with some bloody stuff out of the ambulance box.

Then the next thing I hear, the helicopter come over and this feller, he come down on a winch and they put me in one of those sort of crib things where they lay you down and tie you in so you don't fall out. But, oh shit, I was more frightened of having to hang from that wire, eh. The wire's only as thick as a bloody pencil and it's not only got to hold you but it's also got to hold somebody else as well, hasn't it? And when you're laying there, dangling in bloody midair, if the wire breaks there's only one way to go and that's down, and it was a long way down. And what's more, I'd already been down there and hadn't made much of a fist of that, had I? So when they started to winch me up I said to the bloke that come up with me, I said, 'I hope that bloody wire don't break.'

'You needn't worry,' he said, 'it won't break.' Which didn't help ease my fears one iota, I can tell you.

Anyhow, they got me onto the helicopter and they took me to Cairns Base Hospital and I was in there for near on a couple of months while they tried to fix me up. And all the bloody papers in the world came there to interview me, but I was that bad I couldn't talk to any of them. That's how bad I was. But I remember seeing on the *Cairns Post*, it had in big letters: 'Lucky Worker Cheats Death'. And they were pretty right, too. I should've been dead because the section car, well, it was just squashed to smithereens.

So all that happened on the Queen's Birthday holiday. I'll never forget it. Five doctors and a specialist told me I wouldn't be getting around too much after two years. They reckoned I'd be pretty stuffed by then. Well, I proved them wrong, didn't I, because I went back to work, didn't I. But that was only for a while then I had to retire because being a track section supervisor requires a lot of walking and I just couldn't do it anymore. So they gave me the golden handshake and I got out.

But even now, I still suffer in the knees. Then down one side of me leg it's still sort of numb. I guess the nerves must never have grown back together. But in some ways, I think that's what saves me a lot, too, you know, because I can't feel the pain so bad. Like, I do feel it sometimes but not as often as I should, I don't think.

Memories of a Ganger's Daughter

Back in the 1920s, as a young girl I lived in a small town in western New South Wales where my father was the ganger over three men whom he termed as 'fettlers'. These men had a 'length' of rail line to tender, I think it was about 13 miles either side of the railway station, and they travelled along that distance on a rail trike. Now this trike was a contraption that ran on the railway tracks and it had a flat base for the driver to sit on and a plank for the workers, and to get it going you had a handle to pull back and forward and two pedals to push with your feet.

Our house—well, it wasn't much more than a hut, really—was built on government land on the outskirts of town. Everybody knew it as the 'Ganger's House', and the land it was on was termed the 'railway paddock'. Because my father was employed by the railways he had the privilege of renting this land for one shilling per year. He didn't pay any rates or anything. Now, how much land he had I never really knew, except that it seemed to go on forever. But to give you some idea, it was large enough for him to build a racecourse on and there was also a dam there for the horses. As you may guess, he loved his racehorses.

The Ganger's House was made from boards and logs, with the logs cut in half like they do in a log home, and there was lots of corrugated iron. Then we had three bedrooms and a kitchen. One bedroom, known as 'Dad's Room', was joined to the kitchen and there was a breezeway between there and the other two bedrooms. The breezeway was an open space, with a roof over it. In fact, it was more of a communal area because that's where we ate and drank and washed and all those sorts of things.

Then as far as our family went, there was ... well, my mother had nine children ... wait a minute ... one died and Lorna went to live with Mrs Rawson, so there would've been at least seven children in the house at most times. And in summer we'd move our old iron-framed beds outside to sleep under the stars, and Mum and Dad had one of those big old-fashioned iron beds with, perhaps it was porcelain knobs on it. Oh, it was lovely.

But oh, the snakes. Dad always used to say that the house was built on a bed of snakes, and he was right. I remember when my eldest sister, Jean, put her hand on a snake, on the railing inside this breezeway and she jumped so high that by the time she came down again the jolly thing had disappeared.

'I'll get that snake,' Dad vowed. So he put this poison in a saucer of milk and he took up his position in his rocking chair with a loaded gun waiting for this snake to come out, so he'd shoot it. Anyhow, we left him sitting there and went to bed and when we come out in the morning, all the milk had all gone and Dad had fallen asleep with the gun over his shoulder.

But my father was such a tough old fellow, as maybe many of those old railway fellows were. He used to pull his own teeth and he didn't believe in doctors. Though there was one time when he crushed the top knuckle of his pointer finger while he was out on the railway track. I don't know exactly what happened, but he somehow got it caught in the trike. Anyhow, as I said, he was very fond of his horses—well, more than fond really, and he believed that what was good enough for the horses was good enough for him. So if any of the horses had anything wrong with a hoof he'd treat it with bluestone, which was some sort of acid that came in the form of a crystal. So he put a dab of this bluestone on this crushed finger but, instead of curing it, the finger became infected. Then to counteract the effects of the bluestone he put caustic soda on it, and the combination of the two ate right through the top of his finger. Anyway, Dad ended up going to the doctor with that.

But oh, he was very sick there for a while. And I'm not sure how strict he was on his fettlers but he was so strict with us that we were never allowed out. But you know what kids are like: we sensed that, with Dad being in so much pain, he wouldn't have time to worry about us. So we'd go into his room and say, 'Dad, we're just going up to Turner's' or 'Dad, we're just going off somewhere' and it'd be alright.

Then one night we went in his room and we said, 'Dad, we're just going up to Turner's.'

'Like bloody hell yer are,' he said, and so he must've been getting better by then.

Then Dad's boss was his brother, a railway inspector, over at Bogan Gate. And because of that, Dad had quite a few privileges. So, say, if he wanted to take his horses to Dubbo or Wellington, or he wanted to go with Mum down to the Easter yearling sales in Sydney, his brother always gave him the time off and they'd go. At times like that, all us kids were left at home in our little ganger's house and Jean, our eldest, would look after us.

Jean was a wonderful person, actually. She couldn't have been anymore than twelve, at the most. But see, back in the late 1920s, it wasn't uncommon for someone that young to look after the other children in the family. Anyhow, this particular time, Jean was still at school and Mum and Dad went down to these yearling sales in Sydney. Now, how many of us were there? There was Ted, myself, Marge and Riley, so there was five of us, including Jean. I think the baby went down to Nan's. Anyhow, that's when we got the prowler.

Now, I'm going back about eighty years or so and, back then, you never closed your windows or anything. We only had one room with a door that locked, and that was Dad's room. So there we were in our little ganger's hut, being looked after by Jean, and one night this fellow came prowling around. He might've been drunk or whatever, but he sure frightened us. And in those days there was always a gun lying around the house, just in case of snakes. So Jean got the gun, then she hounded us into Dad's room and she locked the door. Anyhow, through the window, we could just make out this fellow sneaking towards us. So Jean shouted out, 'Go away or I'll shoot!'

Of course, the prowler knew that we were just kids so he crept closer and closer.

'Go away or I'll shoot,' Jean called out again.

Well, this prowler thought it was all a great joke. But then Jean fired the gun and I've never seen someone move so fast. He was off like a shot.

Old 308

I was a fireman with the West Australian Government Railways during the late 1940s, into the '50s, and I still remember that particular day, back in 1949. I'd fired old Es 308 for the fast goods run home, from Katanning to Albany. My driver was the late Stan 'Basher' Weir. Basher was a sports-minded person who loved a challenge, and even though he wasn't my regular driver, I always looked forward to firing for him. Mind you, that could well have had more to do with his wife's excellent cooking rather than Basher being any sort of a considerate driver. See, at that time, I was a young bloke living in the Goldfield's Coffee Palace—a boarding house which was run by two young women, Hazel and Yvonne—and for me to be able to get the chance to taste Mrs Weir's fresh homemade cakes, apple pies and the like, from Basher's tuckerbox, was a delicious bonus from my normal fare.

Anyhow, food aside, our guard that day was Alex Thomson. Alex was a laconic older fellow who constantly smoked cigarettes in one of those long thin holders. I don't remember much more about him, except he had a good-looking daughter, something that could've also been a possible bonus for a young bloke like me.

Now, just after the war there were industrial disputes on the Collie coalfields and we often ended up with a bunker full of uncleaned, open-cut coal containing large pieces of shale and mud. Of course, all that rubbish should've been discarded at the mine site. But it wasn't so the fireman had to sort the good from the bad, which made it a battle to maintain a decent fire.

However, on this particular occasion, we were lucky enough to have a bunker full of the best coal available from the Griffin mine. In normal circumstances you could get by with the fire dancing on the bars, but this stuff was best fired light and often. The tender was fitted with wooden 'hungry boards' to increase carrying capacity, and I took advantage of this quality coal by putting on a good fire then topping up the bunker and footplate from the coal stage.

So we took old 308 out only to find that the Albany Express was running late behind us and was just leaving Woodanilling, 13 miles away. I had on a good fire and a full pot and we were all set for our departure but then the stationmaster began worrying that, if he let us go, we may further delay the express.

'We've got a full swag on, Jimmy,' Basher said to me. 'Do yer reckon we could beat the bludgers to Broomehill?'

'You're the boss,' I said, 'but it'd be a pity to waste this good fire.'

'I might be the boss but you've gotta do all the work.'

So I gave Basher the nod and after receiving a firm warning from the stationmaster how he'd have our blood if we caused a further minute's delay to the express, we set off. And we went like billyo. We flew over the Murdong bank, where some trains halved their loads, and on to Broomehill, 12 miles to the south. Anyhow, we arrived there in such good time that we reckoned we'd be able to make it to Tambellup before being overtaken by the express. So off we went again, with me working like a thrashing machine. And when we reached Tambellup, Basher said, 'I reckon we can make it to Wansbrough.' And we did.

Then out of Wansbrough we steamed on our way to Cranbrook. Crossing the Pootenup Flats, Basher swung the door—the first and only time a driver ever done that for me. But it allowed me to get on a reasonable fire and grab a feed on the run. So we went out of Cranbrook, on to Kendenup then down a bank of sixteen curves to Carbarup and up to Mount Barker, with the express hard on our heels. As we rattled out of Mount Barker, down past the cemetery and over the main highway, the old 308 was bounding around so violently that the cab filled with the asbestos dust and fibres that'd been shaken loose from the boiler lagging. I was clinging on so tightly to the cab side that I later discovered heavy bruising all down my left side.

'Hang on there, Jimmy,' Basher called with a nervous laugh. 'She's got more rattles than a millionaire's baby.'

When we arrived at Narrikup, old Alex Thomson,

our guard, came and handed me the staff to Elleker. As he did, he slid his long cigarette holder from his mouth, shook the ash from it, and said in that long, laconic voice of his, 'Jimmy, do yer know of any pregnant ladies who'd like ta be sure of havin' a little girl?'

'No, why?' I said.

'Well,' he replied, 'if yer do come across any, get 'em to ride in the van behind Basher. I reckon he could shake the nuts out of anything.'

So we left old Alex there, and past Elleker it was usually a roll into Albany. But on this occasion Basher only shut off as we pounded past the loco depot. The entire depot staff must've heard us coming, because they rushed out of the shed to see us go by. Then as we freewheeled over the points and through the narrow granite cutting into Albany, I was thinking, 'God, what a mess there'd be if we derailed and ploughed into all that rock.'

Anyhow, on arrival in Albany, we heard that the express had just passed thorough Elleker, not far behind us. And that was the fastest goods run of my life, by a long shot. We'd cut about two hours off the normal time, completing the trip, with a load, in just a few minutes over passenger time. And large amounts of our own ash and cinders covered our wagons and tarps. We'd used— perhaps 'misused' may be a better way of putting it—all the coal I'd taken on back at Katanning, much to the disgust of our fuelman, Jack O'Keefe, who had to shovel a full 7 tons into the tender, when a normal trip only required half that amount.

Then as we stabled old 308 we noticed that the heads of the rivets, protruding from the frames, had been rubbed smooth and polished by the action of the driving wheels. Also there were gouge marks on the frames themselves, caused as we rocked and rolled down from Mount Barker. And those scars still remain. You can see them for yourself if you visit the Australian Railway Historical Society's museum at Bassendean, because that old 308 is the only engine of her class, of 65 units that had been built in Britain at the turn of the century, surviving to this day. And well, if that old 308 could survive a trip like that, I reckon she could just about survive anything.

On Yer Bike

I first joined the West Australian Government Railways, at East Perth, as a cleaner. That was in August 1946, and my daily wage was 12 shillings and 10 pence. Then when I was transferred to Albany, in December of that year, my wage was reduced by a penny a day; though that's another story.

But one of the real characters down at Albany was old George Smith. Now, other than being the stationmaster's clerk, George was also one of the world's greatest bulldusters, unhung. You could guarantee that if you told him something in the very strictest of confidence, it'd spread faster than a gale-assisted bushfire. To boot, he took particular pleasure in targeting us new blokes with his outrageous tales and, of course, I'd fallen victim to him on many occasions, hook, line and sinker. So I vowed that, one of these days, I'd put one over him.

Then one Friday in late March 1948 I booked in at the loco depot to fire up to Katanning. As it was payday we'd all arrived at Albany railway station a bit earlier than normal to collect our pay. Now, to give you some idea, my Notice of Assessment from the Commonwealth Taxation Office for the year ending 30 June 1947 stated that I'd earned the grand sum of £206, or roughly $412. Now, by today's standards that may seem a miserable sum but, back then, for an eighteen-year-old it was a considerable amount, so much so that I was the envy of many friends in ordinary jobs who earned only half that amount. But, of course, what they failed to realise was that my wage included tuckerbox allowances, a night work penalty for getting into and out of bed at all ungodly hours, overtime and so on and so forth.

Anyhow, that day, my driver and I were rostered to work the Katanning shunter for half a day on the Saturday then work the passenger back to Albany on the Sunday. As it was my intention to go to the pictures at Katanning on the Saturday night, I also took along a small suitcase. Anyhow, this case not only contained a clean change of clothes but also £26 in cash and my tax refund cheque of five pounds, five shillings and ninepence. Now I'd like to make the point here that I'd been desperately keen to save this money because I'd promised my widowed mother a special Mother's Day plane trip to Brisbane to visit my sister, who she hadn't seen for years, and also her grand-daughter, whom she'd never seen.

All went as planned. I'd gone to the pictures in Katanning—so I'd used my suitcase—and we arrived back at Albany on Sunday morning, as scheduled. Then when I opened the locker behind the driver to get out my suitcase, it was missing. A frantic discussion then took place between my driver and myself, such as, 'Who put the suitcase in … are you sure you put it in … did you leave it on the Katanning platform?'

Now, I remembered having seen the locker door open as we were rolling out of Broomehill and I'd simply gone over and shut it without looking inside. We then deduced that the case and its valuable contents must've gone missing somewhere between Katanning and south of Broomehill.

A Katanning crew was due out of Albany with a fast goods that Sunday, so I told them what'd happened and I threw my trusty Malvern Star bike and myself into the guard's van and we set off in search of my case. The plan was to ride in the guard's van to Tambellup, then on the footplate to Broomehill. I knew the road—track—well and I was pretty certain of where I'd closed the door. So when we got near that location the driver slowed the train to a crawl and we kept a lookout. By that stage it was about 21.30, so it was fairly dark, and I was worried that we wouldn't see it. But just then, the three of us simultaneously spotted the case. I jumped off, grabbed it, and to my great relief everything was intact, money and all.

Anyhow, we continued on and we eventually arrived at Katanning at about 22.30 hours, where I went to the railway barracks and got into the same bed I'd vacated earlier that morning. But the thing was, I now needed to get back to Albany as soon as humanly possible. So I slept for about three hours then I went over and settled in the doorway of the local newsagent to wait for the Bay's

Newspaper delivery utility to arrive from Perth. At that time, Bay's were considered to be the fastest road delivery service to Albany. Anyhow, Bay's duly arrived and I explained my position to the driver.

'Sorry, mate,' he said, 'the cab's full of magazines, but you and your pushbike might be able to fit in the back.'

'Okay,' I said. 'Thanks.' And I jumped in the back of the ute with my bike.

Now the Bay's utility was an F100-type Ford with a canvas canopy and a rolled-up blind at the back. The only trouble was, the roads weren't sealed at that time and the dust and exhaust fumes were continually being sucked into the canopy. So, by the time we arrived at Kendenup, I was almost ready to abandon the ute and ride the rest of the way. But I didn't, and we duly arrived in Albany.

'Thanks,' I said to the driver, and I strapped the suitcase to the handlebars and rode my bike down York Street and into the railway yards at 07.00 hours.

As it happened, the first person I came across was old George Smith. Now, George knew all about my loss and how I'd gone out looking for the suitcase. The only thing he didn't know was that I'd just caught a lift back to Albany in Bay's ute. So here was my chance.

'Where did yer find the suitcase?' he asked.

So I told him. Then I said, 'Look, George, I'll see yer later. I really need to get some rest now because I've just ridden my bike all the way back from Broomehill.'

'Blimey,' he said. 'You mean that you rode yer bike all that way, in that short'a time.'

'Yep,' I said.

Well, true to form, my epic ride, through the dead of the night, from Broomehill back to Albany, in better time than a fast goods, spread like wildfire. What's more, until the truth was discovered, George's version grew to such proportions that he likened it to Paul Revere's famous horse ride, through a night in 1775, to warn the colonialists of the arrival of the British troops, at the start of the American Revolution.

One Shot

Well, the last section of the track didn't get built up to Alice Springs until the late 1920s, so it must've been during the '30s when my dad was cooking for gangers and fettlers along the old Ghan railway line. By the end of his time, he'd worked at almost every small town and railway siding from Curdimurka right through to Alice Springs—Curdimurka being just north of Marree and Ewaninga's the last siding, about 20 miles south, before you get to the Alice.

I think the final place he worked at was Oodnadatta, and he was there for quite a few years. At Oodnadatta, I remember he had this huge walk-in cool safe. It worked on the same principle as the old Coolgardie safe, where the water gravitates down through bags and the air cools the water through capillary action—exactly like the old waterbags. Well, he had a walk-in one of them, so he'd kill his sheep or whatever and hang them up in there and he'd also store whatever vegetables he could lay his hands on. Of course, vegetables weren't readily available in the

outback, back then. Dad reckoned that's why so many of
the old railway men got piles—'Lack'a vegetables, son,'
he'd say to me. 'Lack'a vegetables.' I mean, in his mind, it
had nothing to do with a lot of them spending more time
sitting down on their bums than what they did standing
up on their feet that did it. Anyhow, piles aside, it was
quite cool in the cool safe compared to the outside. Well, I
mean, I guess it had to be, seeing that Oodnadatta's one of
the hottest places in Australia.

Anyhow, before Oodnadatta, Mum and I used to live
in Alice Springs and the only time I got to see my father
was during the school holidays, when we'd go down and
stay in whatever railway camp he was cooking at. But, I
mean, there wasn't that much for a young kid like me to
do out there really, apart from going out shooting rabbits.
And I got into enough strife doing that, I can tell you.

See, one particular school holidays we'd gone down to
Ewaninga to visit Dad and there was another young
feller there by the name of Freddy A'Chee. Freddy was a
half-caste and his father was the ganger there at the time.
Freddy was also very well known in Alice Springs. He's
dead now.

But Freddy and me were only kids back then. I guess I
would've only been about eleven years old, if I was even
that. Anyhow, I had a single-shot Steven's .22, so Freddy
and me decided to go out rabbiting, about a quarter of a
mile out the back of the Ewaninga camp. There was a bit
of a sandy knob—a small hill—there, with lots of rabbit
burrows running through it. So we got to this knob and
Freddy and me, we pushed all the rabbit burrows in with

our feet. See, the idea with rabbiting is to block up all their escape routes bar one and you waited at that open hole for them to come out and then, *Bang!*, you shot them.

Anyhow, I'm waiting at this bloody open hole and I hear this rabbit coming up the tunnel, *Thump ... thump ... thump*. So, to save a bullet, I just shoved me bloody hand in the hole to grab the rabbit as it was about to come out. The only problem was that a bloody big brown snake was coming up ahead of the rabbit and the brownie bit me on the arm just above the elbow.

Of course, in those days, you used to cut snakebites to let the poison bleed out. The only trouble was, I didn't have a knife or anything, so I just put the gun to where I was bitten and I pulled the bloody trigger and, *Bang!*, I blew a great bloody hole in me arm. And God, I bled like a stuck pig, which, mind you, probably saved me life. But me arm went all numb, so I didn't feel a bloody thing there for about an hour. But then, when it started to thaw out, holy shit, the pain struck.

Anyway, Freddy and me, we nicked off back to the camp and my dad poured Condy's crystals into the hole in me arm, then they rushed me into Alice Springs hospital in a section car. The section cars were what the navvies—the workmen—used to run along the track. Anyhow, I was in Alice Springs hospital there for three days until I became alright.

So that was one event that happened when I went visiting Dad down along the old Ghan track, back when I was a kid. And I've still got a bloody great big scar there, where the bullet went through me arm, just to prove it.

Oops-a-daisy

It was your typical bush town, set off the highway, with only two partly bitumenised roads in and out of the place. One was coming in from the highway, going down the main street, past a couple of houses, our shop, the bank, then the pub, before dissolving into a dirt track and going out by the old church and heading off beside the railway line on its way to yet another smaller town. The other started out as a dirt track and it came in from some outlying wheat and sheep properties, past the footy oval, across the creek, before it turned into tar and went down, past a couple of houses and met the main street as a T-junction. Tucked into the undersides of the T-junction, and facing each other across the road, was the pub and the bank. If you went over the T-junction you'd end up in the gravel parking area of the railway station. Beyond that stood the silos.

Anyhow, each and every Saturday afternoon old Ted'd jump in his farm ute—one of those big, high-roofed things—and he'd drive from his farm, past the footy oval, over the creek, down the street to the T-junction and, more importantly, to the pub. Now he'd been doing this ever since I can remember and, ever since I can remember, he used to get as pissed as a newt each and every one of those Saturday nights.

But old Ted had worked out a strategy. See, because he knew he was going to get pissed, the first thing he did on his arrival in town was drive over the T-junction, into the gravel parking area of the railway station, do a U-ie, then drive back over the T-junction and park outside the bank which, as I mentioned, was over the street from the pub. With the ute now pointing in the direction of his home, he was safe in the knowledge that, later that night, he'd be able to stagger blindly outside, slip into the driver's seat, turn the key, start her up, and the ute'd head back down the street, across the creek, past the footy oval and down the dirt track, leading to his property. Of course, this'd been going on for so long that the locals used to joke about how old Ted's ute had more brains that what Ted did because it could drive its own way home.

Anyhow, we happened to own the shop that was beside the bank, which was across the road from the pub, and I remember the incident very clearly. I would've been—oh, I don't know—in that thirteen- to fourteen-year-old age bracket. I was in me early teen years, anyway. It was winter—footy season—and we must've had a home grand final because on that particular Saturday there were cars everywhere around the pub. So when old Ted arrived for his Saturday night piss-up he found all his usual spots were taken and he ended up having to park on the pub side of the road, which meant that his ute was pointing away from his home rather than towards it.

Now, it must've been quite late, about nine or ten o'clock at night. I was in me pyjamas, ready to go to bed, and Mum said, 'Shut the shop door up.' So I went out the front to shut the door and that's when I heard all this ruckus coming from over the pub. And as you do when you're a kid, even on such a cold night as it was, I was drawn to the noise from the pub. But then, just as I got to the bank corner, old Ted's ute flashed by, heading in the wrong direction, and I watched as it went straight through the T-junction, straight into the railway yard, straight up the ramp, onto the platform and it crash-landed, nose first, down onto the railway line, leaving its back wheels hanging in midair.

So I run over to the pub to get Dad. 'Old Ted's just drove over the railway platform.' Of course, with everyone being well stonkered by that stage, I was met with calls of 'bullshit', or words to that effect. Anyhow, after a bit, they must've somehow realised that I was fair dinkum because they grabbed their beers and we all wandered over to the railway station. And sure enough, there was old Ted's ute, perched with its nose down on the railway tracks and its back wheels still spinning above the platform.

On surveying the situation, the blokes started scratching their heads and muttering swearwords and the like. Then someone clambered down from the platform, had a look in the cab of the ute and called out,

'Christ, old Ted's not here.' This caused a few more swearwords to be uttered until we heard old Ted's drunken voice coming from behind us. 'Oops-a-daisy, yer silly old coot. Oops-a-daisy, yer silly old coot.' And there's old Ted, he's sitting near one of those potted bushes that they always had on the railway stations and he's mumbling away to himself, 'Oops-a-daisy, yer silly old coot. Oops-a-daisy, yer silly old coot.'

Anyhow, the decision then had to be made as to the best way of dislodging the ute from off the railway platform and railway tracks. Of course, by this stage, with all these blokes having been in the pub for quite a few hours, old Ted wasn't the only one that was as pissed as a newt. They all were, so much so that I'd reckon if you popped the question as to who'd won that afternoon's grand final, the vast majority of them would've already forgotten. So when they all started trying to shout each other down with their own particular rescue plan for Ted's ute, the discussion soon turned into a complete rabble.

But out from that rabble, a unanimous agreement was somehow reached that it'd very much help in the decision-making process if some more liquid refreshments were to be provided. So the publican went back over to the pub and brought back a crate of beer and everyone stood around and had another drink, while they tried to sort the problem out.

The first rescue plan decided upon was to pull the vehicle back up onto the railway platform. So someone got in the ute, started her up and stuck her in reverse, while the others gathered around ready to lift. That didn't work. The ute had back-wheel drive and, with the back wheels still being stuck 3 foot in the air, it was impossible for them to get any traction on the ground. What's more, with everyone having been weakened by the effects of the alcohol, the front of the ute proved too heavy to lift, anyway.

After the first effort had failed, the publican was sent back to the pub to get more liquid refreshments to help work things out. And it was while they were halfway through the second lot of beer that a train whistle pierced the night.

'Christ,' Dad shouted, 'that's the South West Mail. It was due through here yesterday.'

'Typical fuckin' railways,' someone replied.

Just then a bright light appeared down the railway track and a much louder whistle sounded and, in that instant, this group of men went from being as drunk as a mob of skunks into becoming as sober as a mob of judges. Someone dived into old Ted's ute, started it up and planted the accelerator. There was a crunch of gears and a howl from the engine. Smoke belched out from the exhaust. Wheels were spinning madly in the air. Blokes started pushing. Blokes started pulling. There were blokes shouting like crazy. Then another train whistle sounded and I was blinded by its bright lights.

I don't know exactly what happened next because I took off and hid in the ticket office. But I heard a lot of swearing. I heard a lot of crunching and banging. I smelt a lot of exhaust smoke and tyre rubber. Then, as the

South West Mail thundered by, I heard a lot of cheering. And when I reappeared, the ute had somehow managed to escape to safety, over the far side of the railway line, heading toward the silos, and blokes were starting to gather back on the platform.

'I need a bloody drink,' someone said, which was a suggestion that was unanimously agreed upon.

So, without another word being said, they all wandered back over to the pub, leaving old Ted sitting by the potted bush, muttering, 'Oops-a-daisy, yer silly old coot. Oops-a-daisy, yer silly old coot.'

Paperwork

Now, with the Victorian Railways, the head office was at Spencer Street station, and it became well known by us railway fellows as being either 'Bullshit Castle' or 'The Land of the Walking Dead'. And it was, fair dinkum. I mean, of course, this was well before computers, but all the paper-shufflers that ran around about that place shuffling paper was bloody unreal. You have no idea, all the red tape and bullshit that you had to put into written reports and so on and so forth. It almost blew your nose. Oh, everything was paperwork, paperwork, paperwork. So it was no wonder that we were always making up jokes and carrying on about all the different ways they could invent paperwork at Spencer Street.

I remember one joke. It went like this: there was a beautiful, young blonde lady waiting at Spencer Street station to catch a train to Ballarat. Anyway, she had the need to visit the Ladies Waiting Room and, when she went into the waiting room, she saw this brand-new set of fancy scales. So she went over to the scales and she noticed that it read on the top, 'One Penny Will Read Your Fortune'.

'This sounds alright,' she said. So she stood on the scales and she put a penny in the slot and the scales printed out this piece of paper which read, 'You are eight stone two pounds, blonde, young and beautiful, and you're about to pass wind.'

Well, most of that was spot-on, she had to agree. But as for passing wind, well, that seemed a bit far-fetched. But then, much to her surprise, the instant she stepped off the scales she farted.

'Well,' she thought, 'if the scales knew I was going to pass wind, I wonder what else they can reveal.' So to find out, she jumped back on the scales and she stuck another penny in the slot and this time the scales printed out, 'You are still eight stone two pounds, blonde, young and beautiful. You have just passed wind and now you're about to have wild, passionate sex.'

Well, that was completely impossible. I mean, after all, she was in the Ladies Waiting Room in the centre of Spencer Street station. But then, who should walk into the waiting room by mistake? None other than the most handsome bloke this lady had ever seen. And this woman, she took one look at this bloke and this bloke, he took one look at this woman and before either of them realised it, there they were, in one of the cubicles, having wild, passionate sex.

Then when this fellow had left, the woman staggered out of the cubicle and she went back over to the scales and she rummaged through her purse until she found another penny. So she stood on the scales and put the penny in the slot and the scales printed out, 'You're still eight stone two pounds, blonde, young and beautiful, but with all your farting about and fucking around you've just missed your last train to Ballarat.'

And, oh God, we laughed at that one. But I mean, with all the paperwork they made us do, as I said, it was just bloody unreal. Another time, and this is true, when I was at Hamilton all the animals like the dogs, cats and birds and things had to be carried in the guard's van, not in the carriage. And I can tell you, there have been some disasters, what with dogs falling out of the guard's van door, birds gone missing—presumably flown the coop— cats scratching you and so forth and so on. Anyhow, after a few of these accidents had filtered through to Spencer Street, some enterprising paper-shuffler came up with the bright idea that at each change of crew, which was every 60 miles or so, the new guard had to fill out a continuing report as to the current condition and welfare of every animal in his van.

Anyway, one time, someone sent a dog over from South Australia and it somehow died before it crossed the border. Then at Nhill there was a change over of crew and that's where the Victorian guard discovered that this dog had died. So he wrote on his report, 'Dog dead at Nhill'.

So that was okay. Then at the next change of crew, say, at Horsham, the new guard checked the animals and, when he found the dead dog, he checked back over the previous guard's report then wrote on his report, 'Exact same dog still dead at Horsham.'

Then at the next change of crew, the new guard checked all the animals, saw the dead dog, checked the previous reports and wrote, 'Exact same dog remains still dead at Ararat. Rigor mortis set in. No hope of revival.'

Anyhow, this happened all the way down the line until the train got into Spencer Street, where the animals were finally unloaded and a completion-of-journey report had to be filled out. And when that final report was handed in to the paper-shuffler at Spencer Street, the signing-off guard, who was a bit of a dag, had written, 'Exact same dead dog still remains dead at Spencer Street. No hope of revival. Spirit risen. Carcass rotting. Amen.'

Personal Delivery

Up along the old Ghan railway line there were all these remote railway sidings where, say, five or eight fettlers would live, and it was their responsibility to maintain about 30 miles of track—that's 15 miles to the south and 15 miles to the north of their location. Now the particular bloke who told me this story worked at a little siding called Beresford, which is about 30 miles south of William Creek. As you might be able to imagine, it was an extremely isolated existence because, for starters, out there, roads were either non-existent or were in such poor condition that not too many people had cars and, of course, these fettlers certainly didn't. Their only mode of transport was a government railway's section car, a little motor-driven maintenance vehicle that ran along the track.

To compound their isolation, trains came by so rarely that their supplies—their grog, in particular—used to run out pretty quick. And without a regular supply of grog, things looked crook. But a plan was hatched that will demonstrate the depth and brilliance of your average Australian worker, in this case a small gang of outback fettlers.

Now this gang's only communication with the outside world was through Main Control down at Port Augusta and, of course, the railways hierarchy would've taken an extremely dim view if they'd found out just how much grog these fettlers were actually drinking. So, to that end, the fettlers devised a secret code which they sent to their trusted mates in Main Control who, in turn, forwarded it on to the publican at William Creek. And this secret code informed the publican of the date and time he should watch out for their unmanned section car to arrive.

These fettlers then sat down and they calculated the exact quantity of fuel the section car would use on its 30-mile journey from Beresford to William Creek, taking into account such things as wind direction and velocity, track conditions and so on and so forth. That done, they put that exact amount of fuel in the section car, then they put a little more than an equal amount into a separate fuel can, which they placed in the section car along with an envelope that contained enough money to cover the cost of the purchase. That done, they started her up and waved the unmanned rail vehicle off on its journey.

Now as to why these fettlers sent the section car up the track unmanned, was—or so my mate told me—based on the fact that a human being would take up a hell of a lot of precious grog-space on the homeward journey. Though I'd be more inclined to think they were afraid of sending one of their mates up alone, because they knew that if he was anything like them, he'd most probably spend all the money on grog for himself and forget to come back. Anyhow, whatever the true reason, the section car went unmanned. And, of course, depending on the prevailing conditions, sometimes it ran out of fuel a bit short of William Creek, other times it'd go on a little bit, but most times it'd come to a halt pretty much on the money. And when it arrived, the publican simply went over and stacked the section car up with grog, refilled the tank from the fuel can, took his money, put it in reverse and sent it back to the fettlers—personal delivery.

Brilliant. I mean, something like that could only happen in Australia, couldn't it?

Point On

There was a whole movement in the 1960s of hippies taking to the Hippie Trail and I was one of them. Being English, as I was back then, I started off in the 'old country' and I did the whole lot, from England right through down into India and all that before finally flying into Australia from Singapore. Anyhow, when I landed in Darwin I only had two dollars left. That's right, two dollars. So I was 'on me uppers'.

Now I had an aunty in Sydney so that's where I decided to head. Remember, at this stage, I'm still a pasty-white Englishman. So I'm hitching down the road and this truck driver picks me up. Good. Then as we're going along we're chatting away and he's telling me about this weird landscape that I'm going through. I'd never seen anything like it, small bush timber, endlessly flat, with ant hills and stuff. Then we get to this little stop, a little pub. It's just a shack. By now we're probably 50 or 100 miles down the track from Darwin. I don't exactly know where because I'm completely lost in this vast space. Anyhow, the truck driver says, 'Here's a waterhole.' So he pulls in and he says, 'Come on, time fer a beer.'

'Look,' I said, 'I can't afford a drink. I'm stony broke.'

'Don't be stupid,' he says. 'It's my shout. I'll buy.'

So I had my first beer in Australia and, coming from England where we drank pints, I was disappointed because I'm very thirsty and the beer arrives in these tiny glasses. This is stupid, I thought. This is too easy, you know. So we had a couple or three beers and the truck driver said to the publican, 'See yer', and we were on our way again.

Then a bit further on we come across another little stop, another little shack. 'Great,' says the truck driver, 'another waterhole.'

So he pulls in and we go through the whole thing again. He shouts, I drink. Anyhow, after about three or four stops, I'm finding out that this beer's pretty strong and I'm getting pissed. Then we get to ... I don't know ... Katherine or somewhere, though it might've been further north. Pine Creek, I suspect it was, and he says, 'Now, mate, yer gotta buy yer own in this bar. I can't shout all the time.'

'I haven't got any money,' I said.

And so he pulls out his wallet and he hands me some money. 'There yer go,' he says. 'Don't ferget to shout.'

Well, I'm thinking, this is extraordinary. Anyway, we're in this pub and I'm drinking away, talking to this person and that person in a very drunken sort of way because I'm really pissed by now and the truck driver comes over and he says, 'Mate, I've found yer a job'. And this other bloke, a real bushy, comes up—ragged shorts, you know, battered hat, boots, the whole thing—and he says, 'Are yer ready, mate?'

Of course, by now I'm full of Dutch courage with all this drink, so I say, 'Yeah, I'm ready for anything.'

So I get into his Land Rover and we're driving through the bush and he's got this crate of stubbies and it's my task to open a stubby, hand it to him, open another one and have it myself … open another one, hand it to him, and so on. But by this stage I'm so full of beer and I'm so drunk that, when he's not looking, I'm pouring most of my stubby out the window. Anyhow, we finally get to this place. It's dark. I'm really out of it and I don't have a clue as to where the hell I am, and someone says, 'Yer bed's over there.' So I mumble something that I don't even understand myself and I tumble into bed.

Next morning I wake to someone calling out, 'Come on, get up.'

Well, I've got this terrible hangover, absolutely the worst ever. I have a look around and the accommodation's these tiny little compartments in old railway carriages. They're not on tracks, they're just stuck out in a clearing in the bush. So I stumble out of bed with this huge hangover and the cook says, 'Here's yer breakfast.'

And there's this bloody enormous breakfast—absolutely huge—bacon, eggs, baked beans, steak, sausages, chops, chips, toast, the lot. Everything's fried. Plenty of tomato sauce.

'No thanks,' I said. Then I'm loaded onto this truck with some other young guys and we're taken out to work, and it turned out that the job was railway maintenance. Of course, I only discovered later that it was the infamous Never Never Railway Line, the only true Northern Territory government-run line. But even to a rank amateur it was obvious that it'd been laid some time ago because it was now in need of work—lots of work as I was about to find out.

See, what would happen was, in the gang there were about a dozen backpackers like me who were called navvies or fettlers. We were the slaves. Then there were the Thursday Islanders who were the gangers, the bosses. You never argued with them. Anyhow, two of us navvies, we'd take a big iron bar each, one for each rail—they were longer than a crowbar and had a point—and when the Thursday Islander called out 'Point on', we'd put these iron bars or pointers almost on the rail and we'd start to walk along the track. The Thursday Islander, he'd then squat down and look along the rail so he could see where the point of the iron bar was, relative to any kink or bump in the track. And when he saw there was a bump or a dip or a squiggle he'd tell us to stop, then all us navvies, we'd get to it with crowbars, picks, shovels and so forth and work away until the railway line was straight and level.

Now I don't know who we were employed by, but I must say we did a pretty rough-and-ready job. I mean, the ballast was packed so poorly that it would've crumbled if a train ever went over it and, of course, the first rains would've washed it out. But we just got on with it. We didn't care. The money was good, even if it was hard work. And, of course, the sun's blazing down and I haven't got a hat and I'm pasty-white—well, I was pasty-white. Now I'm looking like a cooked lobster.

Then when we'd finished our allotted section of track each day, the big boss Thursday Islander would drive us back to camp and along the way he'd do a detour and stop at some little bush pub out in the middle of nowhere. There were no houses, just these tiny bush pubs. So we'd have a few drinks before we got back to camp where we'd have an enormous dinner—steak, chops, sausages, heaps of mashed potato, maybe some onion. Everything was fried. Plenty of tomato sauce. It was basic cooking, all the same, with lots and lots of meat. It was very filling. Then we'd be so knackered that we'd just fall into bed and go to sleep.

So that's what I did. I worked on the Never Never Railway. And as I said, even though it was hard work and stinking hot and we did a rough job, it was good money for those days and also, the food and accommodation were thrown in.

Then on my last day, it was a real scorcher, but we could see this big waterhole in the distance. Anyway, we always timed it that we'd finish off our allotted section of track and knock off at five, on the dot. So we reckoned that if we really got stuck into it we'd finish our allotted stretch of track by about three, which meant we'd have two hours to wallow in this nice cool, refreshing waterhole. So there we were, it's as hot as hell, we're sunburned to buggery, we're sweating away, but we're working like Trojans.

'Point on.' And we'd walk on and we'd get a little closer to the waterhole. We hardly looked at what we were doing. Our eyes were set on that waterhole and we're thinking, 'This's going to be oh-so-good.'

Anyhow, it's just on three, it's still as hot as buggery and we've worked our guts out and we're within a stone's throw of the waterhole. Then a cloud of dust appears on the horizon and, just as we'd finished our section of track, the truck pulls up and the big Thursday Islander boss jumps out and he says, 'Come on. Quick. Climb on. We've gotta start another section now.'

Shit. Oh my God, I still have nightmares over that.

Quote Me

In the war years, Ken went firing for my father, then when I was about nineteen years old, I started firing for Ken, and I was with him till I got graded when I was twenty-five. And there was almost a family atmosphere in our cab. Especially when he lost a son, Ken really took me under his wing. His son was going out to take up his first teaching appointment and he was killed in a car accident. So at work, Ken treated me like a son and the thing is, I'll say this now, Ken was a very, very family-orientated man.

But during those six years, I had about a year away from Ken. That's when I was in the 'scroucher link'. Scroucher means you go out driving one day and you're back firing the next day. So I was going out and back, out and back, and in the end Ken said, 'You're getting bounced around, you know.'

'I don't mind that,' I said. 'But here's one thing,' I said, 'for the little bit of driving I'm doing I may as well be back with you, Ken.'

See, I knew Ken wanted a regular mate because, while I was scrouching, he was getting every Tom, Dick and Harry to fire for him and that was bouncing him around, too. So I went back with Ken till I was graded.

But one particular trip I remember was when we were bringing freight from Murray Bridge up to Adelaide. I'd say it was about midnight and we saw spotlighters out in the paddock. I think these blokes were doing a bit of rabbiting, you know. Anyhow, we'd been shot at before so when one spotty came straight in and lit the cab, I pushed myself right back in the seat. My thinking was that if they were going to take a pot shot they'd get the engine and not me. I didn't mind the goods vehicles being hit because that's not going to kill anyone. But there's just Ken and me up front, and the guard wouldn't have known anything about it unless they knocked his window out. So you've got to be very, very wary when there's spotlighters about. Anyway, people had to be whacked in the head to be out at that hour of the night. Only milkies, policemen and railwaymen did that. Nobody else.

Anyway, we got over that and we continued on and we'd just travelled over the main road at Blackwood. Ken had shut off and he'd put it in dynamic—the electric brake. You can ride down the hills at a better speed with that and it saves wear and tear on your blocks. You just give it a tickle every now and again, you know, and you could ride right down, virtually, to Adelaide.

So there we were, about 50 yards from the crossing, where the brickworks start. Next thing you know, I look up and there's these bright lights sailing down on collision course with us. I didn't believe it. For all the world it could've been a UFO. But the thing is, it turned out to be a white Valiant. Anyway, he came down headfirst, then he did a 180-degree spin, so now he's coming boot first, with his tail-lights pointing at us. Then *slam*! He hit our locomotive cab's step chock.

Oh, he wrecked his car. The boot section was ripped completely off. Of course, as quick as a flash, Ken put it in emergency, which dropped the dynamic out and the automatic air brake took effect. He shoved the independent handle over and he hit the sand pedal. Luckily, because we were going so slow, we only took about five or six engine lengths to stop. Ken took one look back down the track and the first thing he said was, 'You'd better get the police.'

It was two dudes with a fifteen-year-old girl. As it turned out, the registered owner wasn't driving the car. But there was bottles and glass everywhere and Ken wanted the cops there because, with booze involved, it exonerated the railways from liabilities, you see.

But how lucky can you be, eh? Nobody was killed. Then when I got back from calling the cops, the owner was standing with the young girl. They were shaking like leaves, ghostly white, and the owner's mate—the one that'd been driving—the police reckoned he 'took a powder'. By that they meant he'd shot through. He probably went into hiding at some friend's place and they put him up for the night to make sure he was stone cold sober when he fronted the police the next day.

So that was a close shave. But, oh, you have them all the time. When I was only a pup, I was driving suburban in a 'red hen', coming into Bowden. This was in clear daylight, you know, and this bloke—he'd have been in the region of forty or fifty—had just emptied his bottle of turps and, I suppose, he'd realised that he's got a drinking problem and he'd had enough, so he was going to end to it all by playing suicide with the train.

The thing is, when I saw this person first move to walk out I started to apply the brakes. Oh, he was sozzled to the eyeballs. But then a mate of his decided to complicate matters by trying to pull him off the track. So this bloke went out to grab the sozzled bloke and the sozzled bloke didn't want to be saved because he was so determined to crack the empty bottle of Four Crown Port over the train; you know, be like the queen, christening a ship. I mean, the only thing he was going to hit was the rail car as it ran over him.

So *Bang!* went the handle into emergency. Luckily we had good brakes and, you know, the thing is, I would've hit him if his mate hadn't dragged him off the tracks just in the nick of time. I tell you, I pulled up so close that I could see the bloodshot in his eyes. You know, get the drift? That's how near it was.

But that put the wind up me. And the guard, well, he wasn't doing a ticket check at the time so he was up the front with me and he was jumping up and down screaming. But the poor fellow, the guard, he was doubly upset because he'd just been through a fatal. But that's what happens, see. Let's put it this way; there's been a lot of accidents and there's just a few of us that've been fortunate, and I've been very fortunate. I've had close squeaks but no fatals. Some haven't been so lucky. The thing is, you know, when people commit suicide on you or you have narrow squeaks, our blokes get the feeling they're trying to attack us personally. The thing is, when you go home, whether you've had a fatal or even a near miss, it lives with you. Quote me on that.

Railway Folklore

I've got a few little stories here. I don't know if you can use them or not but they're sort of a part of railway folklore, so I'm sure they'd make for some fun reading whatever the case.

The first one's about a country lad who came to Sydney to find work. The only trouble was that he wasn't trained for much outside of farming so he decided his best bet was to do a course in travel guide hosting, which he did. Anyhow, on his first day out around the sights of Sydney he was given the job as a guide to a busload of foreign tourists.

First they set out to see the Sydney Harbour Bridge. The young lad, now full of knowledge, proudly stood up and announced to the tourists, 'We are now passing the Sydney Harbour Bridge, colloquially known as the "Coathanger" because of its distinctive shape and design.' Then he went on to tell everyone what year it was built, when it was opened, how long it took to build and all the other relevant details. When he finished talking he sat down feeling quite pleased with his efforts—that was, until there came a loud voice from down the back of the bus, 'Oh, in mar country we would'a built that there bridge ten times larger and in half that time.'

Being mild of manner the lad let the comment be, and next they moved on to the Opera House, where he began his spiel again. 'We are passing the Sydney Opera House, colloquially known as the "Sails" because of its distinctive shape and design.' Then he went on to tell everyone what year it was built, when it was opened, how long it took to build and all the other relevant details. Then just as he'd sat down there came the same loud voice from down the back of the bus, 'Oh, in mar country we would'a built that there opera house ten times larger and in half that time.'

Anyhow, this proved to be the theme of the day. At every attraction they came across the lad would describe the sight, informing his passengers of what year the particular structure was built, when it was opened, how long it took to build and all the other relevant details. And countering his every word, the loud voice from the back of the bus kept repeating that, in his country it would've been built ten times larger and in half the time than it'd taken the Australians.

Towards the end of the tour they were coming back down George Street and they were just passing Central railway station when the same loud voice called out, 'Hey, feller, what's that large building over there?'

Well by this stage the young guide had had enough so he stood up and replied, 'Buggered if I know, mate. It wasn't there this morning.'

Another one in that same vein happened on the North Coast Daylight, going up through the Dungog area. Anyhow, there were a couple of middle-aged big mouths on the train who were going on and on in that extremely annoying way of theirs, about how everything from their country was bigger and better. Oh, they were driving everyone in the carriage crazy, absolutely crazy.

Anyhow, there wasn't a big buffet car on on this particular day. It was tray service and one of the young buffet girls or, to use their official name, 'Train Catering Service Staff', was serving lunch and one of the big mouths said to this youngster, 'Excuse me, mii-sss.'

'Yes, sir?' she said, in a very polite manner.

'Mii-sss,' he said, 'would there be any kaan-garr-oos around here?'

And that youngster, like a shot, she said, 'No, sir, but I know where there's a couple of silly old galahs.'

And these two big mouths couldn't work out why the whole carriage erupted into laughter. That girl almost got a standing ovation.

The next story's about two strangers—a man and a woman—who boarded the Indian Pacific in Adelaide to travel over to Perth. As it turned out, the train was overcrowded and their bookings got mixed up and these two strangers ended up having to share a sleeping berth. Anyhow, as they were crossing the Nullarbor the temperature dropped and the female, who was on the top bunk, asked the male on the bottom bunk, 'Could you please pass me up a blanket, it's cold up here.'

Upon hearing this request, the man in the bottom bunk said, 'I've only got one blanket and I'm using it myself so, no, you can't have it.'

Anyhow, the woman in the top bunk came up with a suggestion. 'Well then,' she said, 'how about we pretend we're married and then we can share the blanket?' To which the reply from the male was, 'What do you mean by "we pretend we're married"?'

'Exactly what I said,' replied the woman.

'Okay then,' the bloke said, 'if that's the case, get yer own bloody blanket.'

Another one's about an old man sitting on a railway bench at Caboolture, just north of Brisbane. He was waiting for his train to arrive when along came a young lad with his hair all spiked up in all different colours and he sat down beside the old man. Anyhow, the old chap kept looking at this lad, long and hard. Then after a while, this constant staring got to the young lad so he said, 'Hey, old man, haven't yer ever done nothin' wild 'n' radical in yer life?'

'Oh yes,' replied the old man. 'Years ago,' he said, 'I was out west, out past Longreach, and I got lost in the scrub for months and I got so lonely and frustrated that I ended up having sex with a western lorikeet.'

'Yeah, 'n' so what?' said the young man.

'Well,' said the old feller, 'I'm just now wondering if you might be me son.'

Then the last one's about a train driver. Now, quite often, train drivers have a reputation for being grumpy and this feller was no exception. Just to give you an example, before I go into my story, there's an old railway friend of mine who used to pen some poems and he wrote this one:

The guard is a man who sits in the van,
in the van at the back of the train.
The driver up front
thinks the guard is a so-and-so
and the guard thinks the driver's the same.

So that'll give you some idea as to the grumpiness of some of these drivers. Anyway, there he was, this engine driver, down in the Hobart shunting yards, sitting in the loco, waiting for his usual fireman to arrive. Anyhow, his fireman's running extremely late, which puts the driver in an even grumpier mood than he's usually in. Then along hurries a young man who jumps up in the cabin and says to the driver, 'I'm yer fireman for the day. Ben's got the flu.'

Well the train driver looks down his nose at this young fireman and he grunts, 'So what's yer name?'

'Charlie, sir.'

'I don't address my firemen by their Christian names, son,' the driver snapped. 'Give me your surname.'

'Darling, sir,' comes the reply from the fireman.

'Okay then, Charlie, start shovelling,' grunted the driver.

Rebel

I've never got on with authority; same as with anyone who pushes me around. Never been able to handle it. I don't know what it is, but it is. That's just the way I am. Like, at sixteen years of age, I started my apprenticeship at Eveleigh Railway Workshops, doing my basic fitting. At that stage they were just beginning to phase out the steam and bring in the first diesel-electric locos. Anyhow, on my first day, one bloke—a big, powerful brute he was—he said, 'Chris, there's a lotta bad stuff happening around here. Watch yerself,' he said. 'A lotta the smaller kids like you are gettin' knocked around.'

And that's exactly what happened. To tell you the truth, I've never seen so much blood flow as I did in those first couple of years on the railways, there at Eveleigh, and all because of all the initiation shit that was rife. With the violence and everything we put up with, it was almost like a slaughterhouse. It was very, very frightening. But it was the railway's fault for putting so many kids together. They should never have done it. Like, that compound they sent us to, they had a chain-wire fence separating the first year boys from the second year boys, and the second years were dead set on getting payback for all the shit they'd gone through the previous year.

Anyhow, I was determined not to be humiliated like that. Never. But I had one incident—well I had lots of them, really—but one of the final ones was when a few of us were being transferred to another section. See, they moved us young apprentices around every three months and if anyone was being transferred, on their last day, the older fellers, well, they gave the younger ones a bit of a send-off, you see.

There was a foreman there who had a little humpy or office, virtually straight underneath the railway line, right on the change. Anyway, I was working with an apprentice from a lower year than me and this apprentice was also moving sections. And the silly bugger, I'd warned him that it was a big no-no to tell anyone we were leaving that day. 'Look,' I said, 'don't tell anyone it's our last day or they'll pounce on us.'

So come lunchtime and I don't know where he's got to. I was looking around but I couldn't see him. Now what he'd done, the silly bugger, was that he'd told the older fellers all about how it was our last day in that section. So they'd taken him over to the pub at lunchtime and they'd filled him up to soften him. And, oh, he was in gaga land when he came back.

So I'm in the office, filling out my work sheet, and this foreman's standing there beside his desk and in come about half a dozen of these big, burly tradesmen, and they're going to give us hell. We were going to be their toys for the afternoon. Anyway, they've dragged this pissed kid in and they've brought some really big buckets of water. Then they start pushing us around, ordering us to strip off and stick our heads in these buckets.

And I said to the apprentice, 'I thought I told you to shut up.'

'I didn't know they'd do this,' he reckoned. Oh, he was shit scared.

So I said to this foreman, who was just standing there beside the desk, watching all this unfold, I said, 'Look, we're only apprentices. Why are you letting this happen to us?'

And the bastard said, 'Well I can't see anything happening.' Like, he was turning a blind eye to what was going on. He said, 'I can't see anything happening at all.'

So I just saw red. And well, this foreman had one of those old-fashioned telephones on his desk, you know, the big black ones, with the big handset. So I said, 'Well, if you can't see anything perhaps you won't feel anything either.'

And I picked up this handset, and *whack*, I smashed him fair in the face with it—like, I hit him full force. When all the tradesmen saw that they jumped back in shock, but just for an instant.

Now I could move pretty fast in those days, so I kicked the buckets of water over and I grabbed this drunk kid and I said, 'Run you bastard, run.' And I dragged him out of the office and we took off with these big fellers coming behind us.

'Just keep running,' I said. 'Don't look back. Run, run, run.'

And Christ we went. Even though he was pissed, I can tell you he was sobering up very quick. Still, I had to virtually drag him across I don't know how many tracks—but on the southern side was the locomotive workshops and on the northern side was the carriage works. So when we reached the dividing fence, I got him up, out, and over the top. And because these bastards weren't as nimble as we were, we got away. And from that day on they reckon I was a mad rebel. They reckoned I was insane and likely to click out on them or something. And they left me alone after that. But how we never got killed that day ... well, I'll never know.

So that's how I got the reputation of being against authority. And that stayed with me. I remember another incident, later on. It was at the running shed—the service centre—in at Central. It was along the same lines there, too. I had this supervisor. He was one of those pedantic sorts of pricks who liked to strut their stuff. Anyhow, this day he was out to reprimand a group of us about some misdemeanour or other—something like he was of the opinion that he never saw anybody on the job or something. So he ordered everyone into his office with the view of giving them a good dressing-down—everyone except me, that is. See, he didn't want me in there because he knew I'd erupt and fuck his meeting up.

So, he wanted to see everyone but me. He didn't want me in his office. The only trouble was that everyone else wanted me to come along. They said, 'No, Chris's no exception, he's gotta come to the meeting, too.' So I did. But instead of standing in a line in front of the prick, like everyone else did, I went around behind him and made myself comfortable, sitting at his desk. So there he is, waving his finger at everyone, going crook at them and they're nodding their heads as if to say, 'Yes, sir, no, sir, three bags full sir.' And while all this sucking up to him is going on, I took me shoes off and put them up on his desk and I said, 'Could I borrow yer pen?'

Anyhow, without even thinking, he pulls his pen out of his pocket and gives it to me then he continued on with his boring-as-shit lecture. But when he saw everyone sniggering, he turned around and he said, 'Parsons, what're you doing?'

I said, 'I'm writing my name on the soles of me shoes.'

'What're you doing that for?' he asked.

'Well,' I said, 'everyone around here seems to want to crawl up your arse, so if I've gotta crawl up there too, at least people will know where I am when they walk past you.'

Well, at that stage, he absolutely erupted. 'I said I didn't want that bastard here,' he shouted. 'I fuckin' hate him,' he said.

So that was the end of the meeting.

Rescued by Train

My name's Ron Potter. I look after the Railway Station Museum, here at Coolgardie. We've got a complete old PMR 729 Class steam train, which was built in Glasgow in 1950. We've got a couple of old carriages—one's the same that was used in the rescue I'm going to tell you about: that's the AC 232, which was built in England in 1899. We've also got a guard's van and so on. So we've got the whole works, really. We've even got a room entirely dedicated to the rescue, with lots of old photos and a model of the goldmine. The only thing we don't have anymore is the old railway track that used to run through town. That's been pulled up and relaid elsewhere. Yes, so basically, we've got a railway museum but no railway track.

How that happened was, back in the old days the train took a bender through Coolgardie before it went on to Kalgoorlie and across the Nullarbor. Then in about 1970, they decided to take the bend out. That's why a train hasn't been through for a while. But thankfully, they haven't taken the bend out of the road and you've still got to come through here if you're travelling that way. So people stop and have a poke around. Oh, it keeps me on the hop. I've processed, through the museum, I'd say, close to a thousand people in the last six weeks. So, yes, it's busy, busy, busy.

Now I guess you want to hear how the train helped rescue the Italian. I've recited it to over 3000 schoolkids now. Mind you, many, many years ago it used to feature in the fourth grade government schools' reading book. So that was back then but, sadly, I don't think kids read books these days. It's all computers and television now. As for me, well, I read every night until my eyes drop out.

The chap's name was Modesto Varischetti. He came from a little town in Italy called Gorno. Now last year, I actually entertained the Mayor of Gorno and some of his councillors when they came out to visit the mine site and have a look around. We had a barbecue. There was thirty of them but only one could speak English. Still, they brought some excellent red wines out so it turned into a bloody good show.

Anyhow, back to the story. The date of the accident was 28 March 1907. I think the company Varischetti was employed by was called Westralia Mines. He was working underground, using a compressed-air rock drill, getting ready for a blast, when a sudden storm hit the area and the mine got flooded. Everyone got out bar Varischetti, who remained trapped up to his waist in water, in a little air pocket, well underground. In the old language he was down 1000 feet.

So when they did a headcount they realised someone was missing, so they tapped on the compressed-air pipes and Varischetti tapped back. So they knew he was alive. But then they had to somehow get him out. With the old pumps they had, it would've taken them at least a month to pump all the water out. By then, of course, Varischetti would've starved to death. So they telegraphed the mines office in Perth, which organised a special train—an R Class 174. Then they got two experienced deep-sea divers and their attendants, who were working on Fremantle harbour, and they bundled them, plus all the equipment they needed, into a AC 232 carriage, then they steamed flat out to Coolgardie. Now that trip took thirteen hours, which remained a record for near on the next fifty years, until the diesels came in.

Anyway, when the train arrived at Coolgardie railway station, all the gear was loaded onto horses and carts and they headed off out to the mine, where the divers took it in turns in going down and starting to clear the way. Now you must appreciate that this was back in 1907, when nobody had heard of scuba diving or anything like that. Back then, they had to wear those great big heavy boots and, you know, full camphor suits, big copper helmets, compressors, air lines, the works. Then on top of that it was an extremely difficult and scary operation because it was pitch black down there and they had to feel their way around fallen timber, mud, rocks and dirt, most of which had to be removed by hand. But eventually, on the third day, one of the divers reached Varischetti's little compartment.

Of course, by this stage, poor old Varischetti hadn't eaten or slept for three days so he was exhausted and delirious. He was in a hell of a state. And when you're like that your mind starts to think all sorts of things. So you can imagine what went through Varischetti's mind when, through the darkness, came the sound of bubbles followed by heavy breathing then, when he reached out to feel what it was, he come across a huge, round metal helmet. I tell you, if he hadn't eaten for three days, you could well guess what he might've done. To put it mildly, he was absolutely petrified.

Anyhow, they managed to settle him down and they brought him some food, you know, sealed-up tins and candles and stuff like that. Of course, they'd also been pumping non-stop all this time so, on the ninth day, the water was low enough for one of the divers to carry Varischetti out of the mine and they took him to hospital. Oh, he was okay, though apparently, it did affect his outlook a little bit. Still and all, he went back underground again so he must've been alright by then— either alright or completely mad; one or the other.

But the rescue was world news. I think the President of Italy even sent the divers a purse full of gold sovereigns. Then they were presented with gold watches, silver tea sets and all sorts of things. Well it was such a dramatic event because of the danger. I mean, if the divers had snagged an air line on a sharp rock or some metal, well, it would've been the end of them. They were even going to make a film of it. I think Sean Connery was signed up for it at one stage but they couldn't get enough finance, so nothing's come of it. You could say that I'm still waiting for the telephone call from the producers asking me if I'd be willing to replace Sean Connery, if you like.

Robbery

Well, I came back from the war in 1946, so this would've been round about '51 or '52. The payroll was going up the Midland Railway Company line to pay the staff, right up to Walkaway. There was a hell of a lot of money; in all, around £17,000 in a safe in the brake van, packed in separate satchels for all the different gangs along the track.

At the time I was the recognised paymaster but I couldn't always go, so when that happened, a substitute paymaster went instead. Now, as it happened, this particular substitute paymaster was a very good mate of the engine driver of that train and every time they both went up with the payroll, when they got to Cullalla, the substitute paymaster always went and had a cup of tea with the driver. Cullalla was just a small siding where the trains stopped to fill up with water. I mean, it'd be the last place on earth where you'd expect a robbery to occur because nothing ever happens out on that sandy-plain bush, you know, nothing.

Anyhow, some fellers got to know that the substitute paymaster always went and had a cup of tea with the driver at Cullalla. So they pinched a couple of pushbikes from the goods shed at Midland, hired a car and went up there and parked about 6 miles south of Cullalla, at Mooliabeenee station. There were three blokes in all: one stayed in the car while the other two rode the pushbikes down to Cullalla to carry out the robbery.

Of course, with the substitute paymaster off having a cup of tea with the driver, they had ample time to jemmy the safe open and remove the money. Then they put all these money satchels into a pillowcase that they found in the brake van. You see, when the paymaster got to Walkaway he'd make a bed up for himself for the overnight stay. So they knocked the pillowcase off and put the money in that.

Anyhow, just before the two robbers got back to Mooliabeenee there was a deluge of rain, which obliterated their tracks. But, apparently, this car had a faulty left-hand back brake. So they drove it out from Mooliabeenee, on the gravel road, heading for the main northern highway and along the way they stopped to hide the money. Now to make sure that nobody could discover their footprints they'd made these slipper sort of things out of rabbit skins. So they put those on their feet and they walked into the bush, past the stands of blackboys—the plants—and they put the pillowcase containing the money into a hole in this big log. Then away they went and they got back to Scarborough that night.

In the meantime, the police were alerted to this robbery. Now there was a old feller, Henry Haughton, a white man, who was a famed tracker. So the police called Henry in and after a tip-off, he tracked the car out of Mooliabeenee, along the gravel road, heading for the highway. Then with the car having the faulty brake, it'd made a slight skid mark where the robbers had stopped, and when Henry saw that he said, 'They definitely stopped here.'

Anyhow, because the robbers had worn the rabbit-skin slippers, Henry couldn't pick up their tracks straightaway. But then he noticed that, as they'd walked through the bush, they'd touched or knocked some of the blackboys, so Henry could follow their trail. Eventually he led the police to this big log and, lo and behold, they discovered the pillowslip with all the money in it. So they took the money back to the Gin Gin police station and, with me being the recognised paymaster, I had to go and check all the satchels of money before they were sent back to the ES&A Bank in Midland. Then we had to go through the whole process of drawing another payroll and the next day, another chap and myself, we took the pay up the line by car.

Now, it's quite a lengthy story how they actually caught these chaps, but a fortnight before the robbery I just happened to be checking a brake van in the marshalling yards, in Midland. It was at night and, anyhow, I inadvertently leant over and knocked a switch in the van that caused the side lights to come on, and I just caught a glimpse of these two suspicious-looking chaps standing alongside the van. Anyhow, when I came back I said to the other accountant, I said, 'Look, Fred, I'm a bit worried about something.'

Then when I told Fred about the two chaps, he said, 'I'll ring the police.'

So Fred rang the police and he got onto the sergeant, a feller called Spike Daniels, and Spike said, 'What, is old Claude getting a bit jittery up there, is he?'

'No, no,' Fred said. 'Claude's a pretty sensible sort of a joker. He's just a bit concerned, that's all.'

So that was that. Anyhow, a fortnight later I was home in bed—it was about half past five in the morning—and a knock came on the door. It was Spike Daniels, and he said, 'Claude, where were you last night?'

I said, 'Hey, wait a minute. I've been in this bloody bed all night. Where do you think I've been?'

'Well, the payroll's gone off,' he said.

That was the first I heard of it. Then later that morning, Spike came over to the office with a mug book and he said, 'Claude, go through that and see if you can recognise anything.'

So I went through the mug book and I said, 'Spike, see those two fellers there, they look very much like the pair I saw around the brake van that night.'

'Okay, good,' he said. 'That's Doyle and Steel.'

Spike then found out that Doyle and Steel were occupying a flat in Scarborough, so they laid in wait. And sure enough, that night, along comes this big Ford. So they arrested Doyle and Steel and they took them to court. But, see, the point that this money had already been retrieved was never mentioned in court and, in those days, if you didn't make any material progress in a case, the accused were released on bail. And that's exactly what happened. Steel and Doyle were released on bail because it couldn't be proven that they had the money.

Of course, now Steel and Doyle thought they were safe. They thought they'd gotten away with the robbery. But Owen Leitch, who ended up Commissioner of Police, and another policeman, they went up and they hid near this log where the money had been stashed. Then a couple of nights later they heard the voices of Steel and Doyle coming through the bush. So they laid quiet until Doyle had shoved his arm up the log, then Owen Leitch and his mate called out, 'Stick 'em up!' or something to that effect.

Oh, they reckoned Doyle threw his arms up so high that he flung himself right over backwards, onto the flat of his back. So they arrested Doyle, but Steel took off in the dark and they couldn't find him. Now Steel was a bloke with massive black hair, well down to near his eyebrows. That's how I come to recognise him from the mug shots that Spike'd given me. Anyhow, the police put it out over the radio that Steel had taken off. Then this woman rang the police and they came over and they saw this chap, who was Steel, walking through a paddock. So they arrested him, and both Doyle and Steel were eventually convicted and, I think, they only got something like six or eight years each.

But during the court case it came out that the third chap, the driver, was named Eric Victor Hessell—or it may've been Hesse, I'm not sure. Well, he'd shot through and no-one could find him. Then about six years later, a policeman who'd had nothing at all to do with the case was on holidays in New Zealand. He was at a hotel and, when he went to have a beer, the hotel proprietor said, 'What are you, a tourist or a terrorist?' And the policeman said, 'No, I'm a policeman, over here from Western Australia.'

Then the bloke said, 'Why?'

And the policeman said, 'No reason, just to enjoy myself.' Then it suddenly struck him and he said, 'Now wait a minute, you're that Hessell feller, aren't you? The one who was involved in that railway robbery.'

And the bloke said, 'Oh, that's water under the bridge.'

'No, it isn't,' the policeman said. 'Nothing's ever under the bridge.'

Anyhow, by that stage I was the accountant at Midland Railway Company, so they contacted us and told us that we had to pay £680 to extradite Hessell back to Western Australia. So they brought him back and the case went on for about six days until the magistrate nearly broke down and cried when he announced that he had to sentence 'such a fine fellow who'd been so misled by these two crooks, Steel and Doyle'. Oh, and look, the magistrate just about had everyone in the court crying, too. Anyhow, I think Hessell got eighteen months. And that put an end to the Midland Railways payroll robbery.

Runaway

Well, I was working for a private mob that was formed over here in the west in 1894 and existed until 1964. Anyhow, we were working a stock train, south out of Mingenew, down to Arrino. I was the guard, then there was the driver and the fireman, and we were pulling about twenty bogies full of sheep, which was a hell of a lot of sheep. Then when we got to the unmanned siding at Yandanooka, as was my duty, I rang back to Mingenew to let them know the line was now clear from Mingenew down to Yandanooka.

Now, the train following us was coming down to Yandanooka to pick up filled wheat trucks. They only had an engine and a van, and they were travelling tender first. By 'tender first', I mean they were actually pushing the tender along instead of pulling it. Now, of course, by travelling tender first, a good deal of their vision was obscured by the tender but the reasoning there was that it made it simpler for them to hook on the wheat trucks at Yandanooka and pull them back to Mingenew as per normal, with the loco going first.

Anyhow, south of Yandanooka there's this very steep hill. It was a misty morning and the rails were extremely slippery. Now even though the loco had sandboxes, with the rails being so slippery, along with our full load of stock, the train just couldn't quite make it to the top. It stopped and it wouldn't go any further. So the driver said to the fireman, 'Look, you go ahead and sand the rails by hand and I'll go back and get a good run-up at this hill.'

'Okay,' said the fireman.

So while the driver reversed the train, the fireman started to sand the track up the hill, then he disappeared over the top to go part way down the other side. The reason for him having to sand part of the downside track was that, of course, you had to get a fair length of the train over the top of the hill before momentum takes over and helps you get down the other side.

Now, all this time, I was in the brake van. So the driver had his second crack at the hill but, again, he just didn't quite make it and so we stopped again. Then when I looked out, I saw the driver getting off the engine and starting to sand the track himself. Well, I'm just sitting in the van so I thought, 'Bugger it, I should do that while he goes back and has another run-up at the hill.'

So I got out of my van, walked up to the driver and I said, 'Hey, give me the shovel. I'll do the sanding while you have another go at the hill.'

'Okay,' he said.

Just then, I happened to turn back. 'Hell, she's moving,' I called out.

He said, 'What's moving?'

'The train,' I said.

Now, if I'd stayed in the brake van I could've applied the brake in there. Simple as that. But I wasn't there. And what the driver had done was, he'd braked the train to stop it and, inadvertently, out of habit, he'd put it back into running position. So, the train started to roll back down the hill, with its twenty bogies full of sheep still attached. Now, at the time, I was only a youngster so I took off after the train and I got to within an arm's length of the front of the engine, to yank the vacuum hose off, which would've applied the brakes, but I failed. So then there was no other choice. I raced straight over to the road, with the driver thumping along behind me, and I stopped the first vehicle that came along, which was a ute.

'Our train's took off,' I shouted to the ute's driver.

Anyhow, my train driver had just reached us by then so he got in the front with the driver, I jumped in the back, and we went like the clappers. Now, the implications of our situation were such that it was no good us trying to catch our runaway train because, at the speed it was travelling, there'd be no chance in hell of boarding it. The big concern was the wheat train. It'd been given the all clear and it was now on direct course with our runaway train. So our only hope to avoid a complete disaster was to somehow get past our train and warn them before the two trains collided.

Now, I don't know if you've been in that part of the

country but that particular section of road is very twisty, curly and hilly. So we'd be driving along and our train would disappear out of sight and then we'd see it again, around the next bend. But we were gaining, and the other side of Yandanooka, we finally overtook our runaway. But then, to our horror, we spotted the wheat train coming down the hill towards us, tender first and almost completely blind as to what was heading rapidly towards it. So we jumped out of the ute and tried to get their attention.

Now, their fireman, Bob Sloper, is still alive so maybe you can get him to take up the story.

Yes, well, we were coming down the other side of the hill from Mingenew, heading to Yandanooka. We were doing a fair pace because we were going out empty to pick up these wheat trucks. But then I saw these people down on the road, waving like mad. So I waved back at them, like you do. But then I thought, 'Gee, they're waving pretty wildly for fellers just wanting to say g'day.' And then I said to the driver, 'Geez, if my eyes weren't so bad I'd swear that one of those fellers over there waving was Fred McKenzie, the guard of the sheep train that's supposed to be well ahead of us.' And, by Christ, on second looks it was Fred. Then I noticed that they were all pointing up ahead of us.

Now, by travelling tender first, as you might imagine, it's very difficult to get a good sight ahead. But when I did, well, here's this bloody train coming around the corner at the rate of knots heading straight for us, sheep wagons and all. So I shouted to my driver, 'There's a bloody train coming at us!'

And I can tell you, it's not funny seeing a ruddy train heading at you, full pelt. I was so scared that the fright of it all made me forget what happened next. I guess the driver must've stuck it in reverse. But God, it was just lucky we were travelling empty because, if we'd had full wagons, we'd have been cleaned up good and proper. But, Fred can take it up from there.

Now, because the wheat train only had an engine and brake van they were able to blow the brake off and go helter-skelter in reverse, back up the hill. Then, as our train chased them up the hill its momentum gradually started to slow down and, when it got to a crawl, their guard jumped off his train and pulled the vacuum hose off ours, making it come to a stop.

But that was a day and a half, I can tell you. Oh, we got threatened with the sack and all. Even the poor fireman did, and he had nothing to do with it. He didn't even know what had happened because, as I said, he'd been left down the track spreading sand on the blind side of the hill.

But I mean, you could imagine his surprise, can't you, wandering back to the top of the hill and there's no bloody train, there's nobody, there's nothing. So he spent the rest of the day sitting on the empty sand bucket, wondering where in the heck every bugger had gone, including his train.

Santa

I always wanted to be on the steam locomotives. Well, they just fascinated me. Even when I was a kid in Kalgoorlie, I'd spent most of my weekends over the loco sheds, on the shunter all day, with the crew. So when I finally joined the railways I could, virtually, already fire a loco, no hassles. The blokes couldn't believe it.

But I didn't join straightaway. First I worked in the mines for a while, in the provision store at Tarcoola. Anyhow, Dad was out there with the railways and I was down with him one day sitting in the road master's office and I saw an application for the railways. So I filled it out as a bit of a joke. Like, I'm five feet, eight inches, so where it asked for my height, I wrote six feet, four inches. Then I said that I was 23 stone. Oh, I wrote down all the bulldust you could ever think of. Anyhow, I must've left the application form lying there in the office and I forgot about it. Then a couple of weeks later Dad said, 'There's a letter here for you, Alf.'

'What do yer mean?' I said. 'I don't write to anybody.'

'It's from the railways,' he said. So I opened it up and it was from the boss in Port Augusta saying if I was desirous of becoming a railway employee could I please fill out the application form in the appropriate manner. So I showed it to Dad and he said, 'What the hell?'

'I don't know,' I said.

'I think you'd better.'

So I said, 'Yeah, I will.'

Then Pat Hayes—he's six feet, four inches—well, both he and I went down to Port Augusta and Mr Roberts called us in and he had a silly grin on his face. 'Which one of youse fellers is Harris?' he said. And I put me hand up and he said, 'Jesus, you've shrunk.'

And so I explained everything to him and he said, 'Do you really want a job with the railways, son?'

'I'm down here, Mr Roberts,' I said, 'so, yes, I do.'

'Well here's the form,' he said. 'Go around and see Dr Furler, have your medicals and come back.'

Well, I didn't know how to fill the bloody form out, you know. Anyhow, I went around and Dr Furler called me in and he said, 'What do you want?'

'I've come in here for a medical for the railways,' I said.

'What's that on the wall?'

I said, 'It looks like a calendar from here.'

He said, 'Touch yer toes.'

I touched me toes.

Then he got the form and he scribbled on it. 'Here you are,' he said, and he handed it back. 'You're fit enough to join the railways.'

So I went back and gave the form to Mr Roberts and he said, 'Alright, son, you're on the train tonight, going over the border into Western Australia, to start work at Rawlinna.'

And I said, 'Okay, fine.'

I was about nineteen years old and that was my first job, out at Rawlinna, on the Transcontinental Line. Rawlinna's about 400 miles east of Kalgoorlie. It's pretty isolated. There would've only been about thirty-five or forty people living there. All railway people. I was a youth cleaner: cleaning engines, calling crews, checking the stand-by loco, cutting sleepers to light the locos up and so forth. But I wasn't doing that for very long before I was out firing the trains. But oh, it was great at Rawlinna. Out of my thirty-eight years on the job, they were two of the happiest of the lot of them. I mean, everybody was just so friendly. You could go to anybody's house for a cup of tea.

But I haven't regretted any part of my life, really. Anyhow, when I came back from Rawlinna I was transferred back to Tarcoola. Then when I said I was going to put in an application to go to Port Pirie, everybody laughed. 'Yer've got no bloody chance, mate,' they said.

See, Pirie's a prestige place because, in their minds, it's somewhere nearer to civilisation. Anyway, I put an application in and, less than a fortnight later, I had the offer to transfer to Pirie. Then I went to Quorn, met my wife, Nancy. So we got married and we came back to Port Augusta and we've got four children. They're all adults now, the youngest one's forty-one years of age.

But, oh, we were so innocent, the wife and I. I mean, we didn't even know what caused babies. The doctor should've told me, shouldn't he?

Then, in about 1960, a good friend of mine—a hell of a nice bloke—Sconney McConnell, he'd done a couple of trips out along the Trans-line as Santa Claus and he said, 'What about you, mate?'

'Oh, no,' I said, 'I'm far too young for that. Get somebody else.'

See, those times two train drivers used to work the Santa trip together out and back on the Tea and Sugar train. But then I received the roster note; 'McConnell/Harris'—because I was a driver at the time, as was Sconney—'travel passenger to Kalgoorlie on the express—return welfare'. And I thought, 'Oh, the mongrel.' So I went up to see the roster guy and he said, 'No, mate, yer going.'

So Sconney done the Santa job and I was his assistant, and we had over 900 children when we worked out on that line on the old Tea and Sugar. The railways supplied the presents, then we had to wrap them all up ourselves, and the Australian Workers Union supplied the cool drinks, the lollies and that. But by hell it was hot. There was no air-conditioning, nothing, and we were climbing over presents to get to our cabin. Anyhow, we're getting close to Rawlinna, on the way back, and poor old Sconney, he looked pretty worn out, so I said, 'Sconney, let's go a couple'a beers to see if that'll brighten yer up.'

The only trouble was, it brightened me up and before I knew it, I'd put the Santa beard on, the gown, the whole works. So I went on with it, and at Rawlinna there was a hell of a dust storm, and God it was hot. Our carriage was right near the station and you could hardly see it for the dust. But all the kids, oh look, they were all laughing and carrying on. And they couldn't get close enough to Santa Claus. They just couldn't get close enough. And they were so appreciative. They all said, 'Thank you, Santa.' And I thought about it after and I said to Sconney, 'By hell those kids were damn well mannered.' They were that nice, and those kids, they thoroughly loved it. And so did Santa, I can tell you.

Then I done a few more camps after Rawlinna and in the finish Sconney couldn't take the gown off me. And anyway, thirty-six trips later, I'm still doing it, even though the numbers have dropped. The railways still supply the basics and then Nancy and I, we get donated toys and that—a doll, or an arm or a leg. Nancy'll wash the clothes and do the doll up and I'll paint a pushbike or whatever, just to give the kids that little bit extra, you know.

So to all those kids out in places like Pimba, Tarcoola, and right across the Trans-line, into Western Australia, to Loongana and Rawlinna, I'm still their Santa and I will be until everything ceases.

Scared Shitless

I joined the railways, here in Parkes, when I was about fifteen years of age, pretty much just out of school. Back then we had a population of about 9000. See, Parkes used to be a big terminal town. The lines crossed east–west, from Sydney, Lithgow, Bathurst, Orange, Parkes, then out to Broken Hill, and also went north–south, virtually, from Brisbane, Dubbo, Parkes, then over to Cootamundra, where it connected to the southern line from Sydney, down to Melbourne.

Anyhow, when we'd finished with our schooling, a few of us kids went to Sydney, where we had a medical and a fairly basic exam of arithmetic and spelling. If you passed, you got a start. So I passed and I come back to Parkes and the first job they gave me was a call boy. See, there wasn't a lot of telephones around back then and, anyway, the workers weren't too keen on having them in their houses because, to their way of thinking, the railways would be ringing them up at all ungodly hours of the day and night. So without phones, the call boy had to jump on his pushbike and ride around, in all sorts of weather, to give the train crews their program for the next day. At night, you'd be there to change any times, or to wake them up and tell them they're still on the same job or whatever.

Then from a call boy I went to an engine cleaner before I worked my way right up until I was a driving inspector, where I graded the young blokes coming through. Then I finished in '85 with back trouble and I had some operations. So that was the end of that.

But when I was a young feller, a couple of things happened that might be of interest. See, they had a coal stage where we unloaded the coal into the steam engine's tenders. A coal stage is like the place where you keep bulk grain, but you kept the coal instead. It was made out of really tall timber poles, about 60 feet high, which held a big timber holding bin. To get the coal up into the bin, you'd put a steam engine on the trailing end of four timber and steel rail trucks and you'd push them up on top of the coal stage and leave them there for the labourers to shovel the coal out, into the holding bin. Then the locos came in underneath and you'd have a chute that you'd lower down into the coal tender. So you'd then pull the lever and the coal gravitated down into the tender.

Anyhow, this was a real frosty morning so the driver got a good run-up to push these coal trucks up onto the coal stage. But, no, the rails were too slippery.

'I'll give her another go,' he said.

So he went back a bit further, gave it the herbs and up he went. The only trouble was, when he got to the level part of the unloading area and applied the brakes, due to the frost on the rails, the engine just skidded and four of the coal trucks went clean over the end of the coal stage. And the only thing that stopped the engine from going over was that the automatic coupling released. Oh, it was a mess. Planks went everywhere, the entrance to the depot was blocked with heaps of coal and the coal stage, well, it was buggered.

And that's true. Then there's another one: this old coal stage was getting to the end of its life and we had this A 60 Class Garratt. A Garratt's a big old 3000 horsepower steam engine. It's monstrous, you know, about 260 ton. They were stoker fed, so an auger-like thing would pull the coal in through a worm, crush it up, then you'd have a steam jet that'd blow it over your firebox and feed the fire.

Anyhow, it was about five in the morning, wintertime, and there was only myself and a pretty old chargeman bloke, there at the depot. A chargeman looks after the depot at night when the boss isn't there. Anyhow, the chargeman sent me over to the coal stage to top up the tender of this Garratt.

The Garratt was already under the coal stage so I lowered the chute into the tender and pulled the lever and the coal started flowing. Then when the tender was full, the driver popped the whistle to signal you to pull the lever back and stop the coal flow. So the driver popped his whistle, I yanked back on the lever and *Snap!*, it broke off and the coal kept flowing. Of course, the driver didn't know the trouble. All he could see was that he was slowly drowning in coal. So he kept on popping his whistle, and the more he popped his whistle, it seemed, the more the coal flowed.

Then by the time the cab was half full of coal, the driver took off, swearing and cursing as he went. So I raced over and I got the chargeman and he came and he took to the lever with a big bar. But he couldn't shut it off neither, and the Garratt started to sink under all this coal. Anyhow, the chargeman just threw the bar down and he stormed off muttering under his breath. Oh, he got real cranky. 'Bugger it,' he said. 'Serves 'em f'n right. If they don't maintain this f'n gear then what else do they f'n expect.'

So there was a real to-do about that. And, of course, the Garratt, she just sat under the coal stage, all smothered in coal, until they shovelled her out.

So there's a couple of stories for you. If people want to read them, it's no skin off their nose. And I mean, it's something for history, you know. Hang on, wait a tick, I've just remembered another one.

Out west, back in those days, a lot of the less used lines ran through unfenced paddocks and, of course, the sheep'd wander around and they'd sleep on the track of a night. Like, for instance, there might be only one train going to Dubbo every second night. So you'd come around a bend and there might be twenty or so sheep on the line sleeping, or just there resting, you know. And you can't stop a train on a sixpence, so you'd often collect a few on your way through.

Now, with a train, you can't see right down in front of you, so you can't see any of the actual contact. All you knew was that you hit something. So, when an accident like that occurred, the farmer contacted the railways and you'd have to fill out a Stock Kill Report so they could claim for compensation. Anyhow, one of the questions on the report read, 'What was the last recalled visual position of the animal?' And the blokes'd write, 'Scared shitless and running.'

Shovel

Well, I joined the railways back in 1952. I didn't intend to. It was a bit of an accident, actually. I just went along to the employment people and they sat me down, gave me an exam and a medical, and I passed the lot, so they said, 'You're in the railways.'

'Okay,' I said, and so I stayed on for thirty-seven years.

The first place I worked at was Meadowbank, a metropolitan station, probably halfway between Hornsby and Central. I was what's called a station assistant, and I just worked on the station, cleaning up the mess and that. Then I went on the clerical side of things.

My first clerical appointment was at Tamworth. That was when we had the 1954 floods. Anyhow, I was up north on holiday so I'd left all me stuff in Sydney and I had to go back down to get that. So there was a train still running from Wallangra, just north of Tenterfield, down to Maitland, where the line had been flooded out. So I got as far as Maitland, then we got a bus through to Newcastle, then caught another train back to Sydney.

But with all the floods up that way, I think it might've been ten or twelve days before they run another train back up north. I'm not real sure on that, but I got the first train out of Sydney, anyway. And oh, the floods were an awful mess. It was horrendous. Maitland nearly got wiped out. They made a film about that; *Newsfront*, I think it was. But I sort of got stuck again and I ended up having to go overland by bus. Then when I finally got to Tamworth, I rang up and I said, 'I'm here.' So I went down and they put me in the goods shed. So, I was sitting there with a few of the fellers and they came along and they sort of confiscated me because they were short of maintenance men. I mean, they normally couldn't have done it because I was clerical, but with all the floods and that, it was called a National Emergency. So, I was sent out with the gangs on what was called 'per-way', which was repairing sections of track that'd been washed away.

That's how I ended up working on the Manilla to Barraba to West Tamworth line. Barraba's a bit west of Tamworth. And on the first day we were loading rocks, for ballast, to put under the rail line that'd been washed away. But see, I'd only ever done clerical work. I wasn't the labouring type and my hands were really soft. Anyhow, we did nine hours of lumping rocks into the lorry, and by the end of the day I'd lost all the skin on my hands.

Then the next day they got this grader sort of thing and they pushed the line up and we packed mud underneath. But as it turned out, with all the mud we'd packed underneath, they couldn't put any ballast on. So then we had to shovel all this bloody mud away before we could get the ballast under.

Anyway, we worked for bloody twelve hours each day. That was our hours, from 6 am till 6 pm, and because we started work so early I couldn't get any breakfast at the hotel where I was staying because they didn't serve breakfast till eight o'clock. Then, by the time I got home at night, you couldn't buy anything. Like, all the shops were shut and that. So if it hadn't been for a few of the old chaps who gave me some food, I would've had a pretty lean time of it.

Anyhow, we worked out there doing this bloody labouring day after day and, I tell you, I nearly cracked. It was bloody hard work, and backbreaking, especially for someone who's only used to doing clerical work. Anyhow, one of the old railway gangers—a great chap he was—he could see that I was really struggling and he took a bit of kindness to me. He said, 'Norm, I'll give yer a hint. When yer hump the shovel,' he said, 'the trick is to find one that you can prop up under yer arm so you can lean on it, just like this.' And he demonstrated how to lean on the shovel. Then he said, 'And once yer've got that worked out, the next trick is to look out into the yonder like yer thinkin' about somethin' real important.'

So I took his word for that, and that's what the railways taught me: a good shovel is one you can rest on. And ever since, all me life, that's been my philosophy. Whenever there's work to be done, I just find the nearest shovel and I tuck it nice and comfortable under me armpit and I lean back and I look out into the distance and I try to make out I'm really thinking hard about something really important.

Shovlin' Shit

Back around the late 1940s, early '50s, I knew a bloke who was a train drover. Now this train drover worked out of bush stockyards throughout the Riverina and Victoria, and it was his responsibility to look after trainloads of stock—mainly sheep—until they'd reached the meatworks near Melbourne. Like, if any of the sheep fell over during transit he'd get them back on their feet again so that they wouldn't get injured or die. Then when the train reached the meatworks he'd supervise the unloading of the sheep before jumping on the next train back bush to repeat the process.

After the train had been unloaded, as you might imagine, the stock trucks would be pretty soiled, with having carried all these sheep. So what the railways did was, they employed someone to 'muck out' the trucks. To put it simply, the job entailed shovlin' the sheep manure out of the stock trucks before giving them a squirt down with a hose so they'd be ready to head back bush for another load, and you'd do that day after day after day.

Now the particular bloke that my train drover mate knew who did this mucking out was a feller called George, and this George was pretty new to the job— what's more, he was a little bit below par as far as intelligence went. I won't draw any conclusions there other than to say, it was the only job he could get with the qualifications he had.

Anyhow, so they could get paid each week, all Victorian railway employees had to fill out a work-report form and on that form they had to write a brief description of the activity they'd undertaken and the number of hours they'd worked at that activity. Then after they'd filled out the form they'd hand it into the accountant who'd check it over then send it into the pay office in Spencer Street, where it'd be processed. So when George filled in his work-report he'd write:

Monday—shovlin' sheep shit—8 hours.
Tuesday—shovlin' sheep shit—8 hours.
Wednesday—shovlin' sheep shit—8 hours.

And so on until he reached Friday.

Now, as my mate told it, the accountant got wind that the pay ladies at the head office, in Spencer Street, were feeling a little uncomfortable with George's continued use of the word 'shit'. It just wasn't done in those days. So the railway's accountant got George into his office to explain the situation. George arrived, fresh from the railway yards, smelling to high heaven. 'Look, George,' the accountant said, 'the ladies in the pay office are a bit disturbed with the use of the word "shit" on your work-report form, so how about you start writing the word "excrement" instead.'

And George said, 'Christ almighty, mate, if I knew how to spell the word "excrement" I wouldn't be stuck out there shovlin' shit, would I?'

Snail

The five foot, three inch broad gauge railway line first came through Mt Mary in 1878 on its way to the end of the line at Morgan, on the Murray River. In those days there was a lot of train traffic because the Port of Morgan, as it was then called, was a very busy river port with paddle steamers serving station properties and towns right up into New South Wales, Victoria and Queensland. That's when there was enough water in the rivers, of course.

Then, by the time I was growing up, Morgan was all but closed as a port but still the railways remained our lifeline. When I started school in the early 1950s, the timetable consisted of a 'Flyer' passenger service, which headed for Morgan at about 9.30 am, returning around 11 am. Then the normal passenger train came in just before midday along with a carriage for general goods, parcels of groceries, bags of potatoes and other perishables.

On Tuesdays and Fridays bread arrived in two big tea-chests covered with a tattered piece of hessian. The loaves were packed in on top of each other with little, if any, wrapping and we'd go down to the station with our sugar bags to take it home. They were mostly double loaves joined together, which were then torn apart. So if you were lucky you got the larger 'half'; if not, bad luck. Pies and pasties were in amongst the bread, in a paper bag. Meat was packed in paper and wrapped in newspaper and placed in a box. There was no cooling, of course, so it was just too bad if it was hot.

Early on Mondays a goods train dropped off any empty trucks or vans that had been pre-ordered and any full ones were picked up when the train returned on Tuesday. This process was repeated on Wednesdays and Thursdays, and on Fridays a goods train went both ways. A goods also went both ways on a Saturday. It was an 'oil burner'—probably a diesel-electric—which were being trialled at the time. But most times the goods were hauled by RX Class type steam locos, with the occasional Mountain type engine being used. The locals used the train to send their produce and livestock. Firewood and charcoal always went by rail. A saw bench continually sawed wood, which was then conveyed by elevators straight into railway wagons. At times up to three saw benches gobbled up huge quantities of green mallee.

Also, I can just remember when a lot of wool and livestock was sent by train. The wool was carted in from the north and also south as far as Koomooloo, Redcliffe and Haylands stations, and the cattle were walked in from Alexandrina station. And it was a real sight to see all the cattle and horsemen making their way through the dust with the cows mooing, whips cracking and men shouting.

Then by the late 1950s people were getting better cars and trucks and a bitumen road connected the Riverland to Eudunda, and beyond, so the writing was on the wall as far as closing the line was concerned. And that's what happened, and since then all the unoccupied houses, the stations and some of the fencing along the road have been sold or demolished. We bought the old timber railway station and used some of the materials for our sheds, and some of the galvanised-iron sheeting had so many coats of paint that it was twice as thick as when new.

But you never forget the smell of burning coal, the hiss of steam and the sound of the whistles. And, of course, there were the characters. One colourful chap was a stationmaster called Ernie. Ernie invented his own style of the English language, continually punctuated by unmentionable P's or Q's. In his spare time he gave haircuts to anyone who dared supply him with a pair of hand clippers. Ernie also had a couple of blocks of land outside town and he developed a habit of sneaking out to attend to his blocks and leaving the office unattended. I remember, one day, finding him pacing up and down the station swearing to high heaven about how some customer or other was delaying him from going out to his property.

Also, at the railway station, you'd usually find a welcoming party of gangers or fettlers, full of savoury jokes and gossip. One particular ganger was a good drawer and he hung many well-pencilled images on the office walls. Then occasionally special work gangs came to do painting and general repairs. They had sleeping vans on the loop line, and they were so slow and lethargic that it took them ages to complete a job. When you saw them walking to work of a morning they'd seem to be, virtually, marching on the spot. Then at knock-off time they'd run back to their vans, probably because their next stop was the hotel.

So nothing seemed to be in much of a hurry for the government-run railways. One particular guard named Carl had the nickname of 'Snail'. He got that name because he'd walk so slow to move the points that you'd have to look twice just to check if he was actually moving. Oh, it seemed to take hours just to brake the train and pick up a couple of trucks of wood. And when that was done, he'd wander over to the office to have a yarn to whoever he could collar, then make a phone call or two before deciding to meander back to his caboose.

But one funny thing: Mt Mary's in a flat between two rises and, one time, some runaway trucks, complete with Carl, fast asleep in the caboose, escaped and headed downhill, with the loco in hot pursuit. And I've often tried to imagine, being a fly on the wall of that caboose, witnessing Carl, who'd spent his every living moment doggedly refusing to move beyond snail pace, suddenly being woken up and sticking his head out the window only to realise that he was being catapulted through life at over a hundred miles per hour.

Socks

When we was kids, everybody going to school, those times, they all wanted to be the engine driver of a train. Any rate, around our way, you always had these train driver fellers who wanted to have a bit of fun. See, what they'd do was, they had a great habit of blowing the whistle and letting the steam off right when they were beside you. They used to laugh like hell when they done that, because it'd make your cattle or your horse or whatever take off in all directions. That's true, I had over a hundred head of cattle go over a fence one time.

But the horses were the worst. Oh hell, that steam'd frighten the devil out of them. They'd bolt every time. I remember one time, I was riding this grey horse and the engine driver blew his whistle, and this grey horse just took off in fright and I couldn't pull him up for three miles. I was only about sixteen or seventeen at the time, and it scared the living hell out of me. But that horse, he just bolted and buggered if I could hold him.

Another time, I had a horse drop dead in the main street. That's true. In a jinker—a spring dray. Mum and Dad and I were sitting there, with the horse in this jinker, waiting at the crossing in town for the train to get out of the way. Any rate, all of a sudden, the train driver let the steam off and that horse, it just froze there for a bit then … *Plop!* … it dropped down, stone dead.

Then another time, I was taking a bull calf and nine sucker pigs to the market for a person. I was going along a road with all of us stacked in the jinker and this joker come along with his train and he let the whistle and the steam off, and this horse—I hadn't had it for that long—it shot up the bank and it tipped me and the nine sucker pigs and the calf out of the jinker, clear upside down.

Any rate, by the time I found me feet, the calf and those nine sucker pigs, they'd took off into a 3-foot-high crop of wheat. Oh hell, I looked all day for them but I couldn't find them anywhere. Any rate, I found out later that they'd run back to where I picked them up from that morning. So much for a day's work, eh?

But you could get a decent price for sucker pigs back in them days. I mean, I ask you, how the bloody hell can we keep going with the wages we're paying? The pig industry's a good example. I've bred pigs all me bloody life. Ever since I was a little kid I was out there helping me mother and me father to feed them. And I've always kept pigs because I remember a German feller saying, 'If you're not making money out of pigs, at least you've got the company of them.' And that's my policy. I always kept pigs because I like them.

Recently, I got a worse price for sucker pigs than what I did way back in 1966. In '66 we used to get around £10 for a sucker and, recently, I sold some at market for just $16. It's bloody unreal. And you know what the problem is, don't you? They've been importing pork for the last ten years. I mean, the daughter got some pork in town and I'll swear it was from Canada. And I should know because I was a butcher for thirteen years so I know my pork when I see it. But the thing is, with all the cheap labour they've got over there, there's no way in the world we can compete. I once got onto a joker who used to work on the portside docks, in Melbourne. Any rate, he knew exactly what I was going on about and he said to me, 'I'm out of it now, but I do know that stuff's not coming in from the Melbourne ports.' He gave me the number of another joker to ring. So I rang this other joker up—he was one of the bosses—and he said, 'If I knew where it was coming in, I'd stop it.'

But I found out. Too right I did. See, apparently, this pork was coming in, somewhere up in Queensland ports in those freezing containers, and then they were bringing them down here in semitrailers. So then I complained to the member of parliament, Barry Wakeland, about how all this pig meat was being imported into Australia and he forwarded all of me letters on to Canberra and, eventually, they started sending me all these letters back, full of rot. Any rate, I'd had enough so I got a pile of these letters and I packed them all up and I sent them to John Howard, and he said that he was aware of what was going on but it was too late to stop it.

So, there you go. It's a hard thing to say, but the amount of people that've gone out of business in the last twenty years, it's unreal. Now, most pig jokers, they've gone broke and the pork's still coming in.

Any rate, the amount of people I got to know, over the years, it's just unreal and, as I said, I had a lot to do with train drivers and most of them were good fellers. They were real good fellers. I know different engine drivers who'd have given you their socks if you had've asked them.

So Cold

Well, John and I lived in the Middle East. We were very young and naïve, without knowing much. I was a general clerk and John was with the British Air Force. Then when his time was up, we had a choice of going to England or to one of the British colonies. We really didn't want to go anywhere where it was cold, so England was definitely out and John thought it was better off not going to South Africa because there could be problems there. Canada, so we heard, was also cold.

When we heard all about the beautiful Australian sunshine, we decided that Sydney was the place for us. So we packed our suitcases and we went to Port Said to wait for a boat. Actually, there were quite a few English people waiting there, all bound for different places. Friends of ours went to New Zealand. Then John met some naval seamen. 'Oh, don't go to Sydney,' they said, 'it's a horrible place. Melbourne is the place to go. It's the best.' We didn't know at that time, of course, that there was a big rivalry between Melbourne and Sydney.

So we went to Melbourne. But Melbourne was the worst place to come to because it was freezing to death from the Middle East. We arrived in July 1947 and, oh, it was so cold. We only had our suitcases: no overcoats, blankets or anything. Nothing was organised. We arrived on the Sunday and somebody came to the boat, at the docks, and gave us the name of a hotel, Mulcahy's Hotel. It was opposite that biscuit factory we sold to the Americans—Arnott's. I can remember that because from the window of our room, that was what we saw. But we couldn't afford to stay there so, the next day, we started looking for accommodation. One of the guys who was on the boat with us, a Maltese fellow, came and said, 'If you go to this-and-this office'—it could have been in Bourke Street, somewhere—'you can get accommodation.'

Naturally, we made a run for that and when we got there the man said, 'Just fill in this form.' And the first thing we read was, 'Unless you have got three children you are not entitled to anything.' But we were just married. We had no children. Then somebody suggested the Salvation Army Hotel—the People's Palace. Even the accommodation there was too expensive, but we decided to stay for a few days and, virtually the next day, John got a job. We were at a meal and Brigadier McManus from the Salvation Army came to our table and he said to John, 'I've been watching you. I've noticed that you don't drink and you don't smoke. Do you think you'd like to have a job with us?'

So that was good. Then we went and got a cheaper room in St Kilda Road. Oh, that was terrible. But it was all we could afford. Then I looked up the paper and there was a vacancy at the Spencer Street offices of the Victorian Railways. So I went over and told the man I was looking for a job and he said, 'You'll have to sit for a test.' And there and then he dictated something and I had to write it in shorthand then type it. Well, even though my spoken English was not so good I had learnt shorthand and typing in the air force, so I had no problem with that. And when I finished he came out and he said, 'Oh, you passed with flying colours. You can have the job.'

So I joined the Victorian Railways. Spencer Street was the big administrative centre. I worked in a section of maybe six or eight people that dealt with transporting livestock all around the state. The offices weren't plush. No carpets, just brown lino, and I can't remember if there were open fires to warm us but it was, oh, so cold. Though I do remember the boss very clearly. He had a little glassed-in room where I used to go and do letters. He was a lovely man. He looked like a farmer. He was tall and very patient. The rest of us were in a bigger room. Mr Jones was one man that worked there. He was very nice also and very, very knowledgeable. He used to bring me books to read. I often wondered whether he was the father of that Barry Jones who was on the quiz.

But there wasn't anyone else from another country in the building, so I was such a novelty. They thought my accent was gorgeous. They even took a photo of me and wrote an article about me to put into their monthly railways magazine. They said I was a newcomer and they mentioned where I came from. There was no prejudice, no friction, none at all. This was before migration really started and John and I were almost like freelancers. There was no help from governments, nowhere to turn to. But we never asked anything from anybody, anyway.

The only thing that baffled me was the strange names of the towns—I couldn't pronounce them. Also a lot of Australian slang and sayings I couldn't understand. I still don't. Australian jokes get lost on me. I remember when we got our block of land, Mr Jones, in the building, said, 'Well, we'll all have to come over and have a working-bee to help set up the garden.' But I didn't know what he meant by 'working-bee' and I didn't like to say that I didn't understand what he meant. If I knew, I would have taken him up on it.

Another time I was invited somewhere and they said for me to 'Bring a plate'. So I brought a plate. Just a plate. Nothing else. See, just like the working-bee, I didn't know that either. It was the same with my neighbour who once decided for us to go and see a movie and, when we stood in the queue to get the tickets, the couple who lived opposite us were there. 'Oh, hello,' they said, 'are you shouting?' Well, I was flabbergasted. I didn't know what that meant. And afterwards I asked my friend, 'Why did he say I was shouting? I wasn't shouting. Why does he think I am shouting?'

But they were lovely people, so I was very sad when I had to leave the railways because pregnant women didn't stay until the end. In those days we didn't flaunt our pregnancies. I remember this skirt I had and it was getting tighter, so I thought I'd cover it by having the zip undone just a little bit. Then when I gave my notice they said, 'Well, don't forget to come back and show us your baby.'

And I thought, 'How on earth did they know I was having a baby?'

That was more than half a century ago now, when the Victorian Railways was my first job in Australia. I can't remember their names but I can still remember their faces, and I can still remember how cold it was.

Standard Eight

Shortly after the war, two colleagues and I were travelling in the western district of Victoria, filming on standard 8 film, and on this occasion we came across a down goods train. Now, I'll just explain what I mean by the use of the word 'down'. A down train is any train running away from Melbourne, and any train going towards Melbourne is called an up train. That applies pretty well throughout Australia except, of course, where a train's eastbound or westbound. But the terms 'down' and 'up' originated from the British train timetable, which was written in such a way that you read down the timetable from London on an outward journey, and up the timetable when returning to London.

Anyway, of course, this down goods was a steam train, so we picked up a road parallel to it and I started filming from the back seat of the car. Now, with the standard 8 equipment, when you put your reel in the camera, it ran down one side for a couple of minutes, then you had to turn the reel over and run it down the other side. So

when the film came back from the processing plant, it
was split down the centre.

Naturally, it was very important to keep the light out
while you were turning the reel over, so after I got to the
end of one side of the film, I placed an air force greatcoat
over my head and shoulders to act as a darkroom. But
while I was opening the camera I noticed that our car
started to slow down so I called out to the fellers, 'God,
don't lose him. I won't be a moment.'

'She's right,' came a voice from the front seat.

But much to my concern they not only ignored my
request but, worse still, they completely stopped. By this
stage I was getting quite annoyed with their antics
because I really didn't want to miss out on filming this
train. So after I put the film back in, I threw the greatcoat
off, all prepared to have a go at these two blokes for
allowing the train to get away and there's the loco, sitting
patiently beside us, with the train crew hanging out the
cab, waiting for me to continue on filming. So that just
illustrates how, back in those days, there was a real
camaraderie between train crews and us rail fans.

Anyhow, later that evening, my friends and I met up
with the cooperative train crew at a place called Dunolly
and they indicated that there was a Victorian Railways
Institute in town. So we were chatting away and the crew
said, 'Well, look, there's an evening on at the institute,
would you care to come along and show us some film?'

So we did, and there was a reasonable gathering of
loco men and others in attendance. Anyhow, we'd taken
film in the area before so we showed some of this

previous footage and, in one particular scene, the locomotive's approaching the camera and, as it goes by, a little bit of mist appears on the lens. Then in another sequence, another train's heading towards us and there's water rushing out of the overflow, from the injector, then down onto the track. Anyhow, there must've been a loco inspector present because a voice called out in quite an authoritative manner, 'I thought I told youse blokes not to waste water.' To which a voice from the back pipes up, 'Oh shut up, Bill, this's an entertainment session not a lecture.'

Now, with that part about changing the film under the air force greatcoat; of course, it was most unusual for trains to stop on a section of track just like that. In fact, even back then the locos had a speed recorder on them and these speed recorders were continually being examined. Therefore, any unauthorised stoppage showed up on the chart and had to be accounted for. Now the standard practice amongst enginemen used to be to write down that they'd had to stop for some reason or other, such as, 'sheep on the line'. And I have no doubt that, in order to justify stopping for us to film them, that's probably what they did.

Stone the Crows

It's very different now but, back in them days, not only all the railway's communications but also all the telephone communications and ABC telecommunications were carried across the Nullarbor by a series of wires strung between telephone poles, which ran beside the railway track. Anyway, because there's no trees on the Nullarbor—in fact, the word Nullarbor means 'no trees'—the crows used to build their nests on the wooden cross arms of these telephone poles. And they were a real bugbear on communications because the nests actually formed what's called a 'loop', and that could bugger the system up quite bad.

Anyhow, a young feller came out through our railway camp, one day. He had a very rich accent so I knew straightaway he was English. He was new to the area so I asked what he was doing and he said he was a linesman. Now, predominantly, a linesman's job was to inspect the telephone poles to make sure the cross arms weren't broken plus other general maintenance. So I said to this Pom, 'Oh, that's good. How long have yer been on the job?'

'Only a couple of weeks,' he said.

Of course, straightaway, being who I am, I said, 'What're yer gonna do?'

'Well, in fact,' he said, 'I've been told by my boss to make sure that I clear the crows' nests off the cross arms.'

Now I knew the boss guy who was in charge of all these linesmen very, very well, you know, so I just hesitated for a second then I said, 'Have yer ever had anything to do with crows before?'

'No, no,' he said. 'But apparently they're much like our English ravens, aren't they?'

'Well, yes, they may look a bit like ravens,' I said, 'but I tell you what, when they're nesting, they're bloody ferocious birds. You want'a be very, very careful because if you start pulling down their nests, they'll bloody attack yer, no doubt about it,' I said. 'They've even been known to kill fellers.'

Of course, I promptly forgot about this little interlude and the Pommy linesman went off to do his thing and I went back to my job, and it must've been, oh, I don't know, six months or so later, when this Pommy feller's boss rang me. He said, 'When you're in bloody town next, mate,' he said, 'I want'a talk to you.'

So next time I was in town I went around to see him and he said, 'What did you tell that bloody Pommy bloke of mine about them crows?' So I told him and he said, 'You stupid bastard,' he said. 'Do you know what you've done? You put the wind up that poor kid so much that he was too scared to go near any of them crows' nests and now the whole bloody communications system's up the bloody creek.'

Stop Eleven!

My name is Trevor Tobin. My father was a steam engine driver so I used to spend my weekends on the engines with him. Oh, I loved it, and I was that anxious to be a driver, you know, but Dad didn't want me to be a driver, he wanted me to get into administration. He reckoned that that was the way to go. So when I was old enough I joined the railways as the lowest of the lowly, a junior worker. That was during the war, when I was fifteen, and I worked in the telegraph office because, in those days, the telephone lines only went as far as Northam and Narrogin, so everything was done by telegraph. I began by delivering telegrams, then I got on the telephones sending telegrams to the different metropolitan railway stations.

After that I was sent to Claremont, on relief. Claremont was a busy little place in those days, so twice a week—Tuesdays and Fridays—I was sent up the signals to clean the kerosene lamps and fill them with kerosene. From memory, there were about thirty-seven semaphore signals at Claremont back then and they were pretty high too, higher than a normal lamp post. And also while I was there I was cleaning the points in the yard.

Then I became a junior clerk and I worked my way up to my first position as a station officer, when I was twenty-one. That was in May 1950 and I was transferred to Wooroloo, in the Darling Range, about 40 miles north-east of Perth, and later I also relieved at Chidlow, a small place nearby. I remember at that time, the rabbit plague was particularly shocking. But as all railwaymen did, with this disaster came an opportunity and, at a place called 'Fifty-four and a Quarter Mile', the signalmen used to trap and sell rabbits. So on a Thursday night, when I was relieving the assistant stationmaster at Chidlow, all the train crews would pop in with their rabbit orders.

So I'd ring these orders through to Fifty-four and a Quarter Mile. Then the next night, when the crews were returning from Northam or York, the signalmen would have all these dead rabbits hanging out on a line, ready to be picked up. I think they were charging something like one shilling and sixpence a pair, which was pretty reasonable for the family weekend roast, I thought.

Those days, working with steam engines, were probably the most exciting five or six years of my forty-one years with the railways. And one of the stories I was going to tell you was when I was acting as assistant stationmaster at Wooroloo. See, No. 112 goods train was the regular daily, what we called a 'roadside pick-up train'. Well, it was coming on the down track to

Wooroloo this night and I had lots of goods to load in the van. Next thing, I hear No. 112 approaching with its whistle blowing and blowing and blowing. So I just thought, 'Perhaps he's trying to tell me he doesn't want to stop because of all the trouble they have going up the grade, out of Wooroloo.'

Well, that was too bad because I'd got all these goods ready to load, you know, so I kept the starting signal at red and they just had to stop at the station. But then, when I looked out, No. 112 was rushing towards the platform and it was only the steam engine. There were no wagons, nothing, only the steam engine, and the driver was screaming out, 'Stop eleven! Stop eleven!'

So I rushed inside the cabin and I threw back the starting signals on the down main. By that stage I knew that No. 11, the Albany-bound, double-headed goods train, was already past the home signal and was fast approaching the platform, on the opposite set of tracks. So then I grabbed the hand lamp and I rushed out and started flashing the red light. Well, the driver of No. 11 had to slap the brakes on because he was really hammering it. Of course, they didn't know what was up and I didn't know what was up, either. Anyhow, No. 11 over-ran the signal but, luckily, it came to a safe stop. I mention a 'safe stop' because, when you put on the emergency braking so suddenly like that, in some circumstances, it can concertina the wagons, which would've been catastrophic.

But I still didn't have the faintest clue why the driver of No. 112 had arrived without the rest of his train. So I rushed back to the other side of the platform and he told me that he'd hit a car, just the other side of the distant signal, and he'd thrown it onto the set of tracks that the No. 11 was travelling up on.

As it turned out, these people had gone for a drive in this brand-new car and they'd gone a bit wide across the level crossing and they'd got stuck in the cattle grid—you know those grids they have at level crossings to stop the stock from getting into railway reserves. Well, this car got stuck in the cattle grid and the driver was frantically flashing his headlights against the oncoming train. Now, obviously the crew weren't keeping a good lookout because the train ploughed straight into the car and, in the process, they threw it onto the middle of the other line.

But the driver of No. 112 knew that No. 11 was about due and he had the presence of mind to uncouple his engine and make a dash for Wooroloo. He didn't even wait to see his guard or anything. And as it turned out, if he'd arrived just two minutes later than he did—just two minutes!—well, No. 11 would've gone straight through the station and there'd have been no chance of stopping it.

String

I left Quorn High School in 1953 and joined the railways as a junior employee in the loco sheds. Back then, Quorn was the narrow gauge centre for the line to Alice Springs. So that's where I started. From there I worked through most of the clerical areas before going into the marketing side of things. Yeah, and then I was involved with the amalgamation of South Australian Railways and the Commonwealth Railways, when they become Australian National. At the end I was a production manager in the transport area, organising timetables, drivers, the maintenance of locomotives, safe working; virtually, trying to make sure all that side of operations was going alright, you know.

Probably the achievement I'm most proud of was organising operations for the first Opera in the Outback, with Dame Kiri. Oh, it was a brilliant night. We had about 4 kilometres of passenger trains up there at Copley. A lot of things went on behind the scenes, you know; just the security issues took huge organisation. So that was a very interesting exercise, one of those one-off things.

But my family's involvement with the railways goes well back. My father worked on the construction of the rail line to Alice Springs then became one of their first employees, as an operating porter, in about 1929. When he and my mother arrived up there, the Alice was only a town of about 186 white people. So they were pioneers in that respect. Anyhow, Dad finally transferred back to Quorn and became a senior engineman. See, how it worked was that the most senior enginemen worked the passenger Ghan, the next senior enginemen worked the next most important train and so on down the line—same with the guards and firemen.

Anyhow, Dad was an engineman on the Ghan for about twenty years, going north every other week, and it was a regular thing for the railway men to take their kids up to Alice Springs during the school holidays, as a bit of a treat, and I always remember my father saying, 'Son, what you see in Alice Springs, stops in Alice Springs.' That's because some of the blokes took on a totally different personality when they got to Alice Springs. Oh, they'd go wild.

But my father told me a quite few stories from those old days—some humorous, some not. One he related, he called the Great Gold Robbery. See, in the 1930s, they used to bring gold from the Tennant Creek mines down to Alice Springs by road before it was railed south to Port Augusta then on to Adelaide. Now to give you the background, the railways had a system where you'd get a 'value parcel', like a gold shipment, and both the guards would witness it being locked in the train's safe at Alice Springs. Then seeing the shipment had to be overseen for the whole trip, at the end of each shift, the guard coming off duty had to sign the key over to the guard coming on duty, who was then supposed to inspect the safe to make sure everything was intact.

Anyhow, when they got to Quorn and opened the safe, the gold wasn't there. It'd disappeared. Obviously, one guard was bent and the other guard was too trusting and he hadn't bothered to check the safe at their changeover. But Dad's theory was that the gold never even left Alice Springs. Yes, it was put into the safe but then, while the trusting guard wasn't looking, the bent guard whipped it out again and gave it back to the truck driver who he was in cahoots with. Oh, it was a big thing. Well, they brought detectives up from Adelaide and everything. They even dug up people's backyards. But, no, the gold was never found. So that crime was never solved and they got away with it.

Now to get the benefit of that I should explain that the train crews worked in relay. You'd have a crew made up of two locomotive drivers, two firemen and two guards, and each one worked seven hours and twenty-one minutes on duty and seven hours and twenty-one minutes off duty, and they'd work those hours continuously until they reached their destination. Now, because there wasn't much room in the guard's van, the crews used to hot-bed. Hot-bedding's when one person gets out of the bed and the other chap gets straight in it.

So that's how they did it and, of course, with people having to work so close and under fairly arduous conditions, sometimes there was friction. Nevertheless, some humour came out of it. See, it was a loose practice for the guards to prepare the meals for those coming off their shift. It wasn't, you know, 'You do this. You do that.' It was just one of those things that'd evolved over time. But one particular guard had a habit of cooking stew throughout the whole trip; stew and nothing else. Anyhow, one driver got a bit jack of this so, when he came off his shift, he called out in a complaining voice, 'Hope I haven't got stew again?'

'Not anymore you haven't,' the guard replied, and he picked up the plate of stew he'd had ready for the driver and he tossed it clean out the window. That was that, the stew went out the window and the driver was left to sort something out for himself. So, those sorts of things might give you an insight into the culture of the railways.

But going up through the Centre, those days, was a far more relaxed trip than these days. Maybe it was the isolation because, when the crews left Quorn, they were virtually out of contact until they reached Alice Springs. That's a fair stretch if you're working continually, seven hours, twenty-one minutes on, and seven hours, twenty-one minutes off, for nearly three days—more, if anything went wrong. And when you got home, you'd have twenty-four hours off, then you'd be employed doing something else before you got back on the next Ghan or the next relay train.

But you do hear some stories. My brother was a driver on the Ghan and, well, they were hot-bedding it as usual but there was this obnoxious fat bloke in the crew who had this revolting habit of sleeping with no clothes on. What's more, he was a terrible snorer; a shocking snorer he was. Nobody could get any sleep when the bloke was in the guard's van.

So, one night, while the obnoxious fat bloke was snoring away in the nude, my brother and a mate put a slipknot in a length of string and they tied that around his thumb. They then put a slipknot around the other end of the string and they put that one around his old feller—you know, his penis. Then, as the train was stopping for the change of shift, my brother and his mate got these two big metal lids and they crept up close to the naked, fat, snoring bloke and *Bang!* ... they smashed the two pan lids together like cymbals, and they took off.

Well, I don't think there's any need to describe the outcome, other than my brother reckons the scream that came out of the guard's van that night just about woke up every dingo in the outback.

Swinging

I joined the railways in 1941 and finished up in '84, and for a good part of that time I was stationed here in Parkes as a guard with the Indian Pacific. The IP, as it was known, runs from Sydney, up through Bathurst, Orange, Parkes, Ivanhoe, Broken Hill, down to Adelaide, back up to Port Augusta then across the Nullarbor to Perth.

Now, on the IP, I had five first class sleeping cars and two economy class sleeping cars to look after. See, they had the staff quarters' carriage, then they had the economy class sleeping cars. They were on the back of the train. So this day we were going back to Sydney and I had to go up to the front to collect luggage or something. Then on the way back I come to one of the economy class sleeping cars and there's this old lady walking down the corridor. Well, she looked a bit lost so I said, 'Where're you going, love?'

'I'm going up to see Mary,' she said.

'Mary?' I asked.

'Yes,' she said, 'I go up there every morning at eleven o'clock for a cup of tea.'

'I'm sorry,' I said, 'but I don't think Mary's on the train.'

'Oh, yes she is,' she said.

Now this happened just out of a place called Menindee, so I got on the radio and I got a bush nurse out to meet us at the station. Anyhow, when the train stopped at Menindee, I got the old lady out on the platform. Then after the bush nurse had taken a look at her she said, 'Here you are, dear, I want you to take these pills.' They were sleeping pills but the lady didn't know that.

'Oh, no, no,' the old lady said, 'only Doctor so-and-so gives me my pills.'

Anyway, one of the waiters heard this so he put his white coat on and he came up to the lady and, when she saw him, she said, 'Oh, hello, Doctor so-and-so. It's good to see you.'

'Yes,' he said. 'Now if you could just take these pills, please, you'll be alright.'

And because she thought the waiter was her usual doctor, she took the sleeping pills. Then we got her back into the carriage and put her back to bed and she slept the rest of the way to Sydney, which would've been about fourteen hours.

But the story there was that her daughter had put her on the train at Perth. 'Oh, you'll be right, Mother,' she said. 'See you later.' And she just left her. And this old lady, she didn't know where she was going to or who was going to pick her up or anything. All she remembered was that she always went for a cup of tea with Mary at eleven o'clock each morning. Then when she arrived in Sydney, nobody was there to meet her. Anyhow, I think they put something over the news broadcasts, and eventually, some relative or other came and claimed her. But, that was terrible, wasn't it?

And I'll tell you another one. See, on the IP there was a club car. On one side was a piano and a bar, with seats all around, where people came up from their carriages to have a few drinks and so forth. Anyway, one day we were coming out of Sydney and there were these two deaf and dumb chaps sitting there. And you know the way they talk with their hands, very quick. So there were these two chaps throwing their hands about like crazy and, of course, we didn't take much notice. Then, suddenly, one of the blokes jumped up and stabbed the other one with a pocket knife.

Anyway, we managed to settle the bloke with the knife down, and one of our car conductors who was trained in first aid looked after the stabbed one. Then we kept them there until we got to Bathurst and the police came and took them away. So you could say that they were having a silent argument or something, but I don't know what it was all about.

Then there was another train, called the Silver City Comet. That used to run between Parkes and Broken Hill. You might've heard of it. So we were between Broken Hill and Ivanhoe, one day, when an old chap came struggling down to the dining car on a crutch, and this poor chap only had one leg. Anyway, after he had his morning tea, he struggled back to his seat. Then just before we got to Ivanhoe, the car conductor came up and said, 'Look, Norm, I think this old bloke's dead.'

So when we got to Ivanhoe, we got the bush nurse out to have a look at him and she confirmed it. 'Yes,' she said, 'he's dead.'

So that was that. But then we had to try and carry this dead one-legged man up the aisle—between the seats—and out through the vestibule, at the end of the railway carriage, to get him into an ambulance. Now, I don't know if you've ever tried to carry a dead, one-legged man or not. Well, I can tell you, it was a complete debacle. Other than him being a deadweight, we just couldn't get a decent grip on just two arms and one leg. So we'd pull him up one way and he'd swing over the other. Then we'd get him back up again and over the other way he'd swing. At one stage the whole lot of us nearly ended up on the floor. Oh, he kept swinging all over the place.

Swore Like a Trooper

Then there was old Tommy Shortland. Christ almighty, he swore like a trooper, did old Tommy. He worked as a foreman in the parcels office at Spencer Street station when I was there, working for the railways. Like, when they delivered the parcels and that, it was Tommy's job to organise the sorting out of them and getting them on whichever train they were going on, north, west or whatever it was. Anyhow, old Tommy, it just come out of him without him even thinking about it.

I remember I was working in the receiving office one morning and an old lady came up to me and she was looking pretty upset. 'Who do I make a complaint to?' she asked.

I said, 'What do you want to make a complaint about?'

'Someone's swearing out the back there,' she said, 'and everyone in the railway station can hear it.'

Of course, I had a pretty fair idea who she was talking about, but to make it seem like I was going to get to the bottom of the matter, I went out into the parcels area and

I called out, 'Hey, fellers, there's a woman here who wants to put in a complaint about someone swearing, so which one of youse was it?'

And Tommy stopped sorting out the parcels and yelled out to his fellow workers, 'Okay you mob'a bastards, quit the fuckin' swearin' or some old duck'll dob yer in the shit.'

Anyhow, I was extremely embarrassed about all this and I didn't know what I was going to say to the lady. But when I turned around she had a wry look on her dial. Like, she wasn't laughing about the swearing before, but after Tommy had called out what he'd just called out, she had a bit of a laugh at that. But I didn't know whether to laugh or not so I just apologised. 'Well,' I said, 'I'm very bloody sorry, love, but he just can't help his-self.'

Anyhow, she just laughed and went away. But you know, it sounded so funny because she was so serious at first. I mean, she could've reported him. But that's the way old Tommy was. He just didn't realise what was coming out of his mouth.

Now don't get me wrong, I'm not saying that Tommy wasn't a nice bloke or nothing, but in many ways he was a real bloody oddball. Yes, he was very loose with his language but, when it came to money, he was as tight as a fish's arsehole. Like, he used to love reading the *Sporting Globe*, I think it was—anyway, that sports newspaper. But he'd never buy one. So anybody who'd bought a *Sporting Globe* during the day, they'd leave it in the office for Tommy to read on his way home. Oh, he loved the *Globe*. It was funny; he didn't like any of the newspapers that had any news in them, he just loved the bloody *Globe*. That was his paper.

Anyhow, this Guido Leoni, a wog chap we also had working with us in the railways parcels office, he used to go home on the same train as Tommy and, one day, just as a joke, we doctored up Tommy's paper. See, we had the *Sporting Globe* and we got a copy of the *Catholic Weekly* and we took the racing section of the *Globe* out and we replaced it with the *Catholic Weekly*.

Then after work, Tommy grabs this newspaper and he goes and he settles himself on the train, ready to go home, and Guido settles right behind him, to gauge his reaction. So the train takes off and Tommy starts to read the bloody paper. Anyhow, after they'd gone a few stations, the carriage gets pretty packed with commuters. But Tommy doesn't notice because he's so engrossed with reading his beloved *Sporting Globe*. Then all of a sudden, he flips over the page and there's this bloody *Catholic Weekly*. Well, Guido told us that Tommy let go with such a spray of swearwords that there were train passengers taking off, out of there, in all directions.

'That'a carriage,' Guido said, 'she'a-vacuate real-a bloody quick.'

Takes Two

When I was twenty I went to see the inspector in Mareeba and he gave me a job up at Lappa Junction working as a fettler in a four-man gang. There was three of us Aboriginal, three out of four. The accommodation was quarters, with three rooms. Then I transferred to a five-man gang at Almaden, on the maintenance section. I was the only Aborigine. There was none of that friction. We all got on well. At Almaden the accommodation was a bond-wood hut. On both sides was a verandah and in the middle was a stove for cooking.

Both Lappa and Almaden are west of Cairns. The rail track branches at Almaden. One line goes up to Chillagoe, to the end of the Mungana Stock Route. The other one goes out to Forsayth to meet the stock coming in from the Gulf.

Then from those ganger days I went to a fourteen-man flying gang. Mareeba was our home depot, and we worked from Cairns to Almaden. We did that heavy work, laying down rails and sleepers and all that stuff.

We were nearly all Aboriginal, you know, just with a couple of white fellers. One was an Italian feller. I don't know how he got there. But when I was in the flying gang we was working at Redlynch one day. It was raining and when it rains we don't go out unless there's an emergency. It was smoko time, so this Jason went over to a little shop, across the road, for a packet of wholemeal biscuits and when he came back he opened it up and there was all these weevils in it.

'Look,' he said, 'these biscuits are full of weasels.'

And he wondered what we was laughing for. Then we tell him that weasels are big animals so they couldn't live in a biscuit.

Then later on there was another feller, Kevin. His job was to travel out on the trolley and fill the graphite grease pots between Redlynch and Mareeba. The pots was a little tank on the inside of the rail, and the train wheels pick the grease up off the rail and it stops the friction on the curves. But this Kevin had a thing about snakes. He hated snakes. Worse still, he thought that snakes hated him, too; that they was all out to get him. One day he was travelling from Koah to Kuranda, through the Barron Gorge, and he saw this taipan snake between the tracks. He panicked and he opened the throttle of his trolley, flat out, and kicked up his legs as he ran over where this snake was so it wouldn't jump up and bite him.

Then as soon as he passed over the snake he took a look back. But he didn't see anything. No snake or nothing. Then he started thinking that the snake must be under the trolley and it was going to get him from there. That really got him scared so, while the trolley was going flat out, he jumped off into the bush. He didn't knock the rope off or put on the brakes or nothing. But when he jumps off, he then thinks, 'Oh, what've I done now? I'm gonna cause an accident.' Because the trolley was disappearing down the track at a rapid rate without him.

So, he decided to run back to where he'd passed a fettler gang, just before he saw the taipan snake. So, he starts running back and he comes around the corner and there's the taipan snake lying in the track. But see, he doesn't know if it's dead or alive and he wasn't going to get close enough to find out, so he gets another fright. So then he has to run up through the bush, around the snake, and all the time he's thinking that the bush is full of snakes, ready to get him. Anyhow, he finally gets back to the gang and they ring through to the stationmaster in Kuranda and he goes out and he puts a sleeper across the track to stop the trolley as it flies through the station. But that gave Kevin a big fright, that day.

But, oh, they were good days. I stayed there a fair time, till about 1981, and now I'm an Aboriginal worker with the Seventh Day Adventists. That's good, too. My area is from Sydney all the way to the tip of Cape York, so you see some rewards. You see some good change in people's lives. I've got a positive outlook for the future, between black and white. If we work together we will change the community. If we don't, nothing will happen. It takes two.

The Boss

Look, I'm in the middle of tasting some of George's homemade wine so I'm a bit pressed for time just at the moment. Now, I did find out some historical facts, but the chronology didn't fit and nobody wanted to own up that they'd been involved. Oh, yes, it's a true story, alright. Isn't it, George? I'll even send down a map which'll show you where the Torrowangee quarries were. Big Melva's Brothel did exist in Broken Hill. I now live in that house. Anyhow, do you want me to read what I've scribbled down so far?

Okay, here goes. It'd rained and it'd rained and it'd rained, then it rained some more, just to get on everyone's goat. Boots were soled, or soiled, two inches thick, with a brown-black muddy conglomerate. The downpour had stalled loading operations at the Torrowangee limestone quarries so the train hadn't gone into Broken Hill for a couple of weeks because, as the boss stated, 'If there's no limestone to deliver then the train doesn't run. It's company policy 'n' that's that.'

The boss was a bastard. Nobody like him. Even Albert Brady's three-legged kelpie hobbled for cover when the boss strode down the street. The boss ruled Torrowangee with an iron fist and an even stronger iron will. And so, the aged train—Beaucephalus, Pegasus (the iron equine)—the town's only link to the outside world, remained in the goods shed, a sad and sorry sight, without fire or steam, its trucks hollow and bare. The driver, the fireman and the guard spent their days sitting on empty fruit boxes, shuffling damp playing cards and puffing on scrag ends of roll-me-owns. The company didn't pay its workers well. It paid the train crew even less.

By Monday, food stocks were running low at Sofield's Grocery and still it was raining. There were murmurs amongst the workers. 'If things keep goin' this way, the unthinkable might happen,' they said.

In times of extremes, outback towns act like magnets to every liar, shearer, thief, roustabout, murderer, cook, cheat, prospector and swaggie, as they drift in to escape whatever their heartache, to cadge a fag, pole a drink, scab some food and, in Torrowangee's case, they were also hoping to escape the deluge by bludging a ride on the train into Broken Hill. Even Abdul the Afghan appeared out of the downpour that Monday, leading his blind camel, and took up camp on the outskirts of Torrowangee.

By Tuesday, Sofield's Grocery had run out of food. Not one scrap remained on the shelf. Not even a crumb, can or canister. Then the unthinkable. 'That's it,' called Ted the publican, a thin and sickly man with a past as long as his arm. 'We've run out of grog!'

The pub sank into a quagmire of despair as Ted was caroused by a protesting cacophony of Gaelic grumbles, Cornish curses, Welsh wails, Aussie oaths, Irish irony and plain old English whingeing. 'It can't be so!' they called.

'But it is,' replied Ted, scratching his arm.

By Wednesday, the townspeople had mustered for the cause and an elected committee of tongue-dried miners and parch-throated hangers-on fronted the boss. 'Sir,' they said, 'the town's outa supplies. We need to get the train into Broken Hill.'

The boss stood to his tallest then looked down upon them as if they were wriggling maggots. 'If there's no limestone to deliver then the train doesn't run. It's company policy 'n' that's that,' he barked.

That night, while the boss dined on roasted chicken and the finest of wines, the people ate the last of their scraps then held another meeting. 'Perhaps he does have a heart,' someone said.

So, by Thursday, a different tack had been decided upon and people began knocking on the boss's door to regale some tale of woe or other. Knock, knock. 'Sir, me wife's about due for our fifth 'n' she needs to get inta Broken Hill hospital quick. Oh, she's in terrible pain.' Knock, knock. 'Sir, I'm supposed ta be getting' married on Saturday in at Broken Hill.' Knock, knock. 'Sir, me poor mother's ailing in the Hill 'n', oh God, I need to be by her side as her spirit rises up inta heaven or she'll never forgive me.'

All to which the boss growled, 'If there's no limestone to deliver then the train doesn't run. It's company policy 'n' that's that.'

In Conrad's *Heart of Darkness* he writes of 'an implacable force brooding over an inscrutable intention'. And so it was in this case, all caused by the grip of the liquid gold, the burning desire to bed Big Melva, the tug of the two-up game. Desperate times need desperate measures. The people met again—the implacable force. A midnight visit to the railway barracks. In-depth discussions. All hush-hush. A little graft and corruption. 'But we'll be sacked,' said the train driver.

'So what?' said the fireman.

'Yeah, yer right,' replied the driver. 'So what.'

The guard stammered, 'If I don't get a drink, I'll die.'

After a hearty lunch that Friday, the boss walked out of his front door and looked down to the end of town. He could just make out Abdul's camel standing in the blinding rain. He stepped off the verandah and strode down the street. At seeing his approach, Albert's three-legged kelpie scampered under the wagon. Bill, Jack and the site foreman, Colin Cook, turned their heads to shield themselves from his piercing gaze. 'G'day, sir,' they mumbled, then took for cover.

The boss looked through the window of the pub. Three or four shearers inside and a couple of layabouts, heads hung, sniffing the memory of alcohol. At the sight of the boss's face, Ted instinctively grabbed a cloth and began wiping some already well-wiped glasses. The boss walked over to Sofield's Grocery. Upon seeing him, young Meredith Worth grabbed a straw broom and began resweeping the bare earth floor.

He idled home satisfied. He had them all exactly where he wanted.

It rained heavily that night. The boss was woken a couple of times by loud cracks of thunder, blinding sheets of lightning. He smiled. 'Good, no train for a few days yet.' Then he rolled back to sleep, as sound as a baby.

Saturday morning, the boss was up early. He felt good. He cooked himself a hearty meal of bacon and eggs. After breakfast, he washed and shaved. He donned his finest suit. He preened his moustache in front of the mirror. 'I'll see how the low life is going, today,' he said to his reflection.

He opened his front door and stepped out onto the verandah. The rain had stopped momentarily. A certain quiet had settled over Torrowangee. The streets lay empty. He couldn't even see Abdul's camel. His pace quickened as he walked along the street to Albert's wagon; no three-legged dog. He put his face to the window of the pub. No, not a sign. He strode over to Sofield's Grocery. A straw broom lay on the floor. Nothing else. Nothing at all. Then, far in the distance he heard a train whistle.

The Christmas Party

Right, the first thing you must realise was that I was only nineteen years old and straight out of Greylands Teachers' College in Perth when I took up my first appointment, out on the Trans-line, at the small railway settlement of Coonana. Coonana's about 300 miles or a six-hour train trip, east of Kalgoorlie.

So the year was 1959 when I took to the rough track out there in a little Standard 10 Vanguard. Trouble was, uncharacteristically, a cyclone had gone well inland and it'd wiped out a lot of Coolgardie and had deposited a whole heap of rain. Of course, anything out there, when it gets rain, it turns to mud. So it was a very difficult trip. I'd slip and slide along until I got to a stretch of water. Then I'd get out, walk about to find a way around it and, when I did, I'd get going again.

Still, I was making reasonable progress until just the other side of Karonie, where I got stuck. I then got out some water, lettuce, a carrot and my briefcase and started to walk. Now this's in the middle of nowhere, you know, and all I knew was, if I kept the railway line to my right and followed the track I'd eventually be alright. So I'd walk, rest, walk, rest, and I would've been going for a couple of hours when I heard this odd sort of calling sound. At first I thought it was a crow. But it wasn't. It was someone, a male, coming up behind me. I'd never met the guy before but he turned out to be the headmaster from Zanthus, a little siding just along from Coonana. He told me that he was bogged back down the bush and he'd left his wife and three-week-old baby in the car, along with his water supply. I mean, he wasn't going to die of thirst anyway because there was plenty of water in the holes in the rocks. But he had nothing else, so we joined up and we walked on until we got to Coonana.

Now, Coonana consisted of twelve houses. That's all. So I started knocking on doors in search of the boss ganger. The odd thing was that every door I knocked on was answered by either an Italian, a Yugoslav, a Greek or what-have-you and, being New Australians, they struggled to understand a word I was saying. What's more, there was no way that they were going to let us past their front door. 'This's all a bit odd,' I thought.

Anyhow, through a process of elimination we finally found the ganger's house. I knocked. The ganger opened the door. 'Hello,' I said, 'I'm the new schoolteacher. This's the headmaster from Zanthus. We're both stuck back down the track. We've had to walk and, as a consequence, we've had nothing to eat.'

Of course, if he'd been Australian he would've said, 'Welcome. Come in and have a beer.' Well, I waited. No answer. The ganger just looked at me blankly, and the longer he looked at me blankly the more I began to realise that he also couldn't understand what I was saying. Then, when he finally noticed that we were covered in mud, he managed to say, 'No water. Water turned off.'

Anyhow, we were somehow led to my quarters, which turned out to be two corrugated-iron rooms. Two water tanks were out the back but the bottoms had been shot out of those so there was no water. However, we did manage to get it across that we were hungry and we got a feed of eggs. So we stayed there that night, then the following day we caught the fast goods train back to Karonie. The guys there were Australian so there were no communication problems and they helped get our cars out of the bogs. But gee, you really had to feel for the headmaster's wife and young child who'd been stuck out there all that time.

So that was my introduction to Coonana. It was the end of January, very hot—made doubly worse because of this cyclone—and there I was, in an extremely isolated part of this great country of ours and I was the only person who could speak English. All the fettlers and so forth were war refugees—'displaced persons' they were known as.

Of course, being the only teacher, my biggest problem was how to communicate with the kids. Bear in mind they ranged from Grade One through to Third Year high school. Now, because the workers came and went so quickly, numbers varied. On average there'd be about twenty students and only some of those had picked up a little English from the previous headmaster. So I very soon learnt the art of mime and gesticulation to get my meaning across, and they did likewise. Lessons were a bit of a scream, really. But those European kids were absolutely gorgeous. I couldn't have had better. They came with nothing and they had nothing. And a lot of them had suffered through a war, which must've been hell, so in a funny sort of way, they were quite happy and content being out there, living in a place like Coonana.

But as I said, my quarters consisted of two corrugated-iron rooms. Out the back was a laundry-washing area. In the front room was a bed, a fridge and an old wood stove. There were no trees around the place so it was hot as Hades in summer. Mind you, it was as cold as charity in winter, too. But it'd be 120 degrees or whatever in the waterbag and I'd come home from work, and if I lit the stove the room was unbearable. So I didn't really do much in the way of cooking. Oh, there was no electricity. We used Tilley lamps.

Anyhow, after a month or so I got glandular fever and ended up in Kalgoorlie hospital for a fortnight. Then when I was about to came back out, the doctor said, 'Now listen, get a crate of Kalgoorlie Stout and even if you don't cook a meal, have a bottle of stout.' And that's what I did. The stout got me through.

Then when I returned to Coonana and started to try and find out where things were, I came across an old radio and a microphone. 'What the devil's this?' I said. Then I discovered an old Royal Flying Doctor (RFDS) medicine chest. I made inquiries about the radio and, yes, it was once commissioned out there. So I got onto the RFDS and they came out and they gave me a new radio, an aerial and they set me up with an in-service course and a new medical chest. I then had the idea of putting the kids on air and for them to send telegrams and messages, and that not only gave them something meaningful and different to do but it also helped with their English.

Now, with being the RFDS contact: I remember one of the ladies was pregnant. 'She's about due.' I said. 'What's going to happen?'

'Oh,' they said, 'she'll go into Kalgoorlie on the Tea and Sugar train.'

But as it turned out, the Commonwealth Railways wouldn't take her on the train because, after seven months, I think it was, they felt she was too far gone. So then they turned to me. 'Well, Graham,' they said, 'you'll have to do the job.'

Now, remember I'm still only a nineteen-year-old kid and my experience of women is negligible. It was like, 'Hell, now I'm going to have to deliver a baby!' Anyhow, I got onto the RFDS and they sent out some books about delivering babies. After reading those, well, I'd lost all confidence. But then, luckily, some rabbit trappers came through in an old four-wheel drive and I asked if they'd take the woman into Kalgoorlie. So, we did a deal and, in exchange for a carton of beer, they agreed to take her in and I was saved from having to deliver a baby. That was a great relief, I can tell you!

Then later on a grader came through grading the edge of the railway track, and I got them to make an airstrip at the back of the school. We all then got together and walked it in emu fashion to pick up anything that was likely to puncture the plane's tyres. So from then on we hooked onto the monthly RFDS visit and they'd fly out and have a clinic.

Anyhow, by that stage we started to have some Australians come in, so another thing I was quite proud of was that on my first Anzac Day, the kids and I, we got an Australian flag, a German flag, a Polish flag and an Italian flag and we ran them all up the pole. Then we sang Anzac Day songs. We had Anzac prayers. We did the 'Lest We Forget'. And no-one had any problems with that because, as far as I was concerned, those people who were at Coonana, like the Germans, the Slavs, the Italians and so forth, they'd been made refugees because of the war and they were here to say, 'Okay, let's all move on from all that.'

But a lot of those refugees, you know, they'd come to Australia with nothing at all and so the Commonwealth Railways provided them with a table, chairs, beds, fridge, all their clothes and food—accommodation. But then, don't forget, all those items were purchased from the Commonwealth Railways shop and, well, by the time they'd deducted what was owing, I've seen these people get their pay packets and there's absolutely nothing in it. Nothing—not a cent. You know that song 'I Owe My Life to the Company Store'? Well, a lot of those refugees owed their lives to the Commonwealth Railways. So when it came to Christmas I said, 'Why can't we have a Christmas party for the kids?' And, of course, they said, 'Well, there's no money.'

Okay, so we ran a few raffles and things and we raised enough money to get some beer out from Kalgoorlie. In those days the beer—big brownies—came out in a crate. We bought presents for all the kids and everyone got dressed up, you know, for this Christmas party. Then because there was no town hall we held it in the school. We had some music and, I mean, it was absolutely brilliant. But one thing, talking about my naivety with all things female. Well, we had a part-Aboriginal lady there and by the time the night got going and we were dancing around the floor, she decided to feed her baby, so she just dropped them out. Well, I'd never even seen a bare-breasted woman before so, oh, I nearly died.

And that Christmas party was the first social get-together ever held in my time at Coonana, and it was great for the kids, great for the parents, great for the community.

The Debutante

I was born in Estonia on 18 December 1927. My childhood was spent on my parents' mixed farm near Parnu. We grew mostly winter wheat. I don't know what they call winter wheat down here, but we put it down late in autumn, so in winter it stays in the ground, then in spring it comes up, no problem. It grows. Also we had a few cattle, about a dozen sheep and a couple of horses. Those days you did all your farm work with horses.

I was in my teenage years when I was taken by force from my parents' home by the German army officers and sent by boat to Germany. I was placed in a youth camp and I did forced labour for the German government. Then they sent me by cattle railway truck to Czechoslovakia.

In Czechoslovakia we were in a prison camp, more or less like that. We didn't work, but one day we were taken out and we were put into this room thing. We didn't know anything about it but I worked out it was a gas chamber. We survived—I don't know why—so we must have been like guinea pigs and they were experimenting because the guards, they came in with us and they were wearing gasmasks.

After the war I was an apprentice, before they came to me to go to either America, Canada or Australia. If I stay in Germany I had to take out German nationality and I didn't want to do that. I reckon it was the British government because we were in the British section of Germany. I think we were what is called 'displaced persons', because there were groups called that who came out here and they had to work for the Australian government for two years. Oh yes, we had to sign a contract and we had to work the work they gave you, not the work you wanted or you were trained for.

But I didn't become a railway worker until later on. When I first came here I went to Bonegilla and was given a job in the kitchen there. But I only stayed at that for four or five months, then I broke my contract. No, there wasn't any penalty at all. But I was learning nothing in Bonegilla and I said, 'I finish. I want to get out and learn something.'

And the boss said, 'Oh no, you can't. We won't let you go. We will send you back to Germany.'

'I don't think so,' I said, because I was stateless, anyway.

So I went fruit picking. I spoke no English before I left Germany, none at all and, oh, the English was very rusty. But that was my priority. I wanted to get out, so I pick it up and learned something. But I pick it up slowly. One day my boss come—there were trees growing all along his driveway—and he give me an axe. 'Cut those trees,' he said.

'Yes, boss,' I said.

'Do you understand me?'

I said, 'Yes, boss, I understand you.'

But I didn't. I misunderstood because he only meant for me to trim the trees and chop those little bits up for firewood. But I cut all his good trees down with the axe. They were sort of like poplar trees. And when he came back in his big car—he had this old Ford or something—well, he wasn't happy. He started shouting at me and I thought, 'Now what's wrong with him?' because I didn't know a word of what he is saying. But I know today, and it wasn't very kind, the words he said. So I got the sack from there and I went to work in a packing shed, and when we finished the fruit packing they said, 'You all have to go to Adelaide Railway School.'

That was 1951. It wasn't my choice, but it made my day. So I was a month or six weeks down there doing a course and then they distributed us all around the stateside. I was sent to Terowie as a signalman. Terowie was a big railway town. There were many people working there because it was where the narrow gauge and the broad gauge met. It's now a ghost town. I think they even shut down the last of the pubs just recently.

Back then, all the coal from Leigh Creek was sent through Terowie on its way to the Electricity Trust. It was all steam trains. The coal came on the narrow gauge from Leigh Creek, and at Terowie it was tipped into broad gauge trucks by railway workers. That was brown coal. They had a sort of tipper, you know, a special lift that tipped the whole truck over, off its wheels, and the coal just went down a chute and into a broad gauge truck underneath.

But the signals were all operated manually by kerosene light. The stationmaster got the phone call that the trains were coming in and, to keep the railway line clear, the signals had to be right. So, it was my job to go and see if the lights were working right and to change the signals so the trains can go through. I had to climb up a ladder, about 20 feet up in the air, and make sure the kerosene lamps were lit. It was shift work because they were going twenty-four hours a day, and behind those lamps were coloured things, like red for stop, green for go.

Us workers, we stayed in cottages just along from the railway station. They were pretty good. You had the meals provided. Of course, they took it all out of our pay, but I really can't remember how much. We got paid when the passenger train came through from Adelaide every second Thursday, and some of the wives of the workers were down there just waiting and when the men got paid those women took the money bag straightaway from their husbands. They didn't want the men to go off and spend it all on grog or something. That's right. Oh, a lot of those things happened.

But I was single then, and I remember in my second year I got quite friendly with one of the Australian families. They were so very good to me, and they had a beautiful daughter. The father worked on the railway.

He was a special engine driver that tipped the coal. Anyway, he come to me one day and he said, 'Jaan, my daughter, she's going to a Deb Ball and she hasn't got a partner.' Then he said, 'How about you taking her and have a night out with her?'

'My,' I thought, 'that is good,' because I knew her too, you know, and she was very beautiful. So I said, 'Oh, yes. I will come to your place and I will pick her up.'

'No, no,' he said, 'I will bring her to the Institute Hall where the ball is being held.'

'Oh, okay,' I said, but I was disappointed because I wanted to pick her up myself.

Anyway, he took her to the Institute Hall and then I took her into the Debutante Ball. And oh, she looked so beautiful, and everything was going so very nicely, and when the ball had finished I said, 'Shall I walk you home?'

'Yes,' she said, 'that would be nice.'

Then when we walked out of the Institute Hall the first person I saw was her father, and he come over and he said, 'Well, I'll take her from here.'

And that was that. But oh, I was so disappointed. I could have gonged him that night.

The End of the Line

Well, I'm into my nineties now, so this is a long time ago that I'm talking about. But as a very young girl, we lived at the end of the line at Tottenham. The nearest railhead was Parkes and that's where we travelled to if we wanted to go anywhere else, you could say, exotic.

Anyhow, I remember that the mixed goods train arrived in Tottenham midafternoon, three days a week, and its arrival, as was its departure, was a big event. On train day, us kids, we'd listen out and when we first heard that distant bleating hum, our excitement levels began to rise as the sounds grew into a rumble. Then, eventually, there'd be a whistle and the train would come into view, puffing smoke. Just about everybody in town gathered at the railway station to greet the train. So we'd meet up with our friends and swap news while at the same time keeping an eagle-eye on who got off and what goods were being unloaded.

We lived along the approach line to town and when the train had finished at the railway station they'd shunt the carriages back along the western side of the line from where we lived, where they'd be left empty overnight. I can remember Mum saying how they were being patronised by young courting couples at night, which caused us to surmise that a few babies were conceived in those vacant carriages. Many was the rumour around town about how some poor girl was pregnant with a 'carriage baby'.

But the process of shunting was extremely dangerous work and more than one life was lost. See, the buffers between the carriages, luggage vans and trucks were linked by heavy chains and the men's timing had to be precise when they were placing these links or else they'd get crushed. Finally, after all the shunting had been completed, the loco was driven onto a turntable where it was reversed, ready for the next morning's return journey.

After the train had settled in for the night, we'd go out along the tracks with a bucket and pick up coal. Now, I'm also sure that the train crew always managed to 'accidentally' drop some coal off along the line for us. But my mother, she'd complain about how the coal made a dirtier fire than what wood does. But we used to like it. We used to like the smell of the coal.

Then because the train's crew had to stay in Tottenham overnight, there was a railway barracks where they slept. The barracks were built quite a distance from us. Well, I suppose, it must've been within easy walking distance because the crew were very often card players and my dad would sit by the front gate in his old rocking chair, waiting for a certain type of coded train whistle which meant that a game was on, and Dad was included.

Of course, a train journey was always a valued experience. There were two main rules: first, was to get on as quickly as possible to avoid having to sit near the toilet. Second, there was a scramble for the seats facing away from where the soot came in through the windows. If there was a hardy male on board he'd more often than not occupy the luggage rack up top, where he could have a snooze and recover from the previous night's card game.

But the train's departure from Tottenham was seldom uneventful. Any occasion of interest, such as a marriage or a birth or some family moving away, was acknowledged by an array of train whistles and either one, two or three detonators being placed on the rails to explode. Weddings were the highest on the whistle and detonator scale. So we'd leave town accompanied by bangs, whistles and clunks before the train settled into its beautiful rhythm of clickety-clacks as we'd gain speed towards Albert, then on to Tullamore.

At Tullamore there was a stopover as the engine had to take on water and some further shunting took place. If you were quick enough to get to the fireman before the engine moved, he'd fill your billy with boiling water for a nice relaxing cup of tea. Still, many thought that the train's water contained a certain taint, so most female passengers preferred to cross the street to the cafe. The men had other priorities. Now, even though it was common knowledge, we still held it as a sacred secret that a two-up game, somehow, happened to coincide with the arrival of the train in Tullamore, so the men would disappear into the hotel, there to try their luck and partake in the local brew.

When the train was ready to continue on its journey, we'd be notified by a blast of steam followed by a big whistle. Then it was fun to just watch the people scurrying across the street. Of course, there were the stragglers—invariably men—who'd been delayed by the last throw of the two-up coins or the final gulp of beer. Nevertheless, with a great jerk and a groan, the train would start moving off without them.

And this business at Tullamore was quite a scream, really. The train would've already left the platform so all the wives or girlfriends, they'd be hanging out the windows screaming for their particular partner to get a move on, and there'd be children in tears, worried that their fathers were going to be left behind. Then, with a huge hiss of steam, the train would brake and slow down. But, of course, because it'd already left the platform there was no way of getting on board other than to be physically hauled up through opened doors and windows. And, oddly enough, on all my trips through Tullamore that was the standard practice.

So, with everyone safely back on board, the train would give another big jerk and start huffing and puffing as it regathered its momentum. Then with a great hiss of steam, it'd fall back into that beautiful clickety-clack rhythm. Through my child's eye, I can still see this huge white cloud coming out of the funnel, you know, rising up like a giant meringue.

The Flea

I had forty-four years with the railways and most of that time I was on the relief staff, working all over the ship. So it's been twenty years since I retired. That was August 1984. I first joined when I was a youngster, way back in the war years, around 1940. That was at Blacktown, in Sydney. It was a bit of a family affair, really. Dad was a signalman, then I joined, and me brother, he joined a bit later on. I was only about sixteen or seventeen and me brother was twelve months or so younger than me. We were both junior station assistants. Them days they called us junior porters.

But about me brother. See, we called him The Flea because he was a real bugger for getting under people's skin and picking fights and all that. I don't know what it was with him but he just loved a fight. And the thing was, he never won too many neither. He used to get belted up pretty bad, sometimes. But that didn't seem to worry him. He just loved picking fights.

There was this day; we were both working on the station and there were these young fellers from

Kingswood. It was a Friday afternoon and The Flea
started giving them a whole lot of crap. You know,
calling them all the names under the sun and really
stirring them up. Then as they jumped on the train they
shouted out, 'We'll be back fer you, yer little bastard,'
which only caused The Flea to give them another
mouthful. 'Yeah, anytime yer piss-weak mob'a bastards,
anytime yer like.' Or words to that effect.

The next night was a Saturday night and, in them
days, Saturday nights was usually very quiet. Anyhow,
I'd forgot all about this until these fellers from
Kingswood turned up again, all geared up to belt the
crap out of me brother. The only trouble was, The Flea
wasn't there. It was just me. So I explained to these
blokes how The Flea wouldn't be back at work until
whatever day it was and whenever time it was. Then one
of the fellers asked how come I knew so much about The
Flea.

'I'm his brother,' I said.

'Oh, well,' they said, 'we may as well bash the crap
outa you then.'

As you might imagine, I wasn't too keen on this and I
wasn't too keen on fighting neither, especially when
there was more of them than there was of me. But see, I
knew that Dad was down the end of the platform and, in
them days, during the war years the lighting on the
platforms was very poor, so I said, 'Well, if you want'a
fight, I'll give you a fight but we can't fight on the
station.' I said, 'Come down the end of the platform and
we can have a bit of a go there.'

That was fine by them. So as we're walking down to the end of the platform to have this big stoush, I called out to me dad, 'Hey, Dick,' I said, 'there's some fellers here who want a fight.'

Of course, they didn't know that Dick was me dad, and Dad was a pretty big bloke, and what's more, he knew how to handle himself. So we get down to the end of the platform, where the light's real dim, and Dad takes about four steps out of the shadows and *whack, whack*, he makes a real meal of these blokes.

Anyhow, the local policeman happened to turn up and when he saw the mess that Dad'd made of these fellers, he said, 'What's going on?' So we told him and he said to these fellers from Kingswood, he said, 'Get on the next train back home 'n' don't come back.'

And they never did come back neither, which was much to the disappointment of The Flea.

Then I remember another thing. This was before The Flea joined the railways with Dad and me. There was another young feller. I forget his name now, but it was still at Blacktown and, as I said, during the war years the lights were so dim on them platforms, you could hardly see.

Anyway, Dad was at the one end of the platform, up in the signal box, and me and this young kid, we were talking down the other end of the platform. I forget what we were on about but we were just chatting away there and a train went past, heading towards the mountains. Then all of a sudden, this young feller, I don't know why but, just as the train heading to the mountains had passed, he jumped down to scoot over to the opposite platform and *Bang!* the poor bugger jumped straight in front of this army special that was coming the other way. And oh, he got cut to pieces. As dead as a doornail he was.

But poor old Dad, he was up in the signal box, so one moment he saw the two of us having a chat on the platform and the next he sees one of us getting scraped along in front of this train, and he didn't know which one of us it was. It was pretty upsetting for him. But this kid, he would've only been about sixteen at that time, the same age as me but, God, he was a mess. He was just like a bag of liver when they came to pick him up.

The Silverton Tramway Company

I know a story about a railway that wasn't called a railway but a tramway. Now, I know that might sound a bit confusing, and the ramifications of all that certainly came to confuse my dear old, departed dad, so I'll try and explain.

Basically, the story of the Silverton Tramway demonstrated the parochial state rivalries we had in the 1800s. See, back in those days we were six separate states and each one of those states ruled its own roost. Then, in the early 1880s they discovered deposits of high-grade silver, lead and zinc around the Silverton area, just north-west of where Broken Hill is today, and before long Silverton became a big boom mining town of about 3000 people.

Of course, they needed somewhere to ship out their ore and Port Pirie, in the Spencer Gulf of South Australia, was obviously the best choice because it already had a shipping wharf. But without a rail link to the Gulf they had to bag the ore in Silverton, load it onto bullock wagons, then haul it all that distance—a process that took over a month.

Anyway, the South Australian government already had a rail line going north through Terowie, before it branched off west, and the South Australians realised the economic benefits of building a rail line right up to Silverton. The only trouble was, the New South Wales government wouldn't allow the South Australians to build an inch beyond the border, and neither were they interested in extending their own rail system from its then railhead at Parkes.

So the South Australians said, 'bugger this', and they started building a three foot, six inch narrow gauge railway line from Terowie, up to their side of the border, at Cockburn. By that stage, a boundary rider named Charles Rasp had discovered ore at Broken Hill. So then the good citizens prevailed upon the New South Wales government to connect the gap between Broken Hill, Silverton and Cockburn. But once again, the New South Wales government refused. No way were they going to maintain an isolated bit of narrow gauge railway, stuck way out on their western border.

This, of course, meant that the process of bagging and hauling the ore had to continue. And even if it was over that shorter distance to Cockburn, it still remained a hassle. So, it got to the point where the good citizens got really mad about the situation and said to the New South Wales government, 'If you won't build a bloody rail line to connect us to the South Australian system then we'll build one ourselves.'

And the New South Wales government said, 'Okay, you can do that but you're not allowed to call it a railway.' That's because, if it proved to be a successful railway system then the politicians from New South Wales would have egg dripping down their stupid faces. And that's when the Silverton Tramway Act of 1886 was passed, which gave them the right to build and operate their own rail line. So they floated a company and they raised something like £500,000.

Then they started building a narrow gauge three foot, six inch rail line, to join Broken Hill to Cockburn, which was compatible with the line from Terowie to Cockburn. It was all pioneer track—called a 'hoop-on' railway—very lightly laid, no ballast, just heaped-up red dust, small rails, sleepers spaced out at 6 foot, with a very low speed limit of around 10 mph and a maximum load of about 6 ton per vehicle. So the Silverton Tramway Company started operating in the late 1880s and it became the richest privately owned 'railway' system in the southern hemisphere. So much for the politicians from New South Wales, eh?

So, it wasn't until the late 1920s or early '30s that the New South Wales Railway's standard gauge four foot, eight and a half inch line was extended from Parkes to Condobolin, before it was carried on to Menindee then across the Darling River. That was also a very lightly laid pioneer track. They didn't even build cuttings, so the train just went up and over everything. She was like 'whoop-de-doo'.

Then when the New South Wales standard gauge line finally arrived in Broken Hill, they built their own station over in Crystal Street while the South Australian narrow gauge line still came in at Sulphide Street station. That meant that the transit passengers were forced to either walk or catch a horse-drawn hansom cab to go the half mile or so from one station to the other to catch their allotted train. Then, of course, with the differing time zones, the clocks and timetables on both railway stations were half an hour different.

And that's where it confused my dear old, departed dad. Mum reckoned that's why we never went to the capital cities when he got his holidays. See, Dad was one of those hardworking miners who, once he got sat, just wanted to stay sat. He liked to keep things nice and simple. And to travel by train was all too much for him because, say, if we were planning to go to Sydney, he had to remember that, even though we lived in Broken Hill, which is in the state of New South Wales, we ran on South Australian time. Then he had to remember to go to the Crystal Street station, not the Sulphide Street station and, if we got to the right station at the right time, we caught the Silver City Comet, which ran on the standard gauge four feet, eight and a half inches, and we travelled the 500 miles to Parkes where we had to change onto the Central West Express, which was the Dubbo train, and when and if we caught the Central West Express, even after all that, we still had a hell of a long way to go before we got to Sydney.

And it was just as bad if we wanted to go to Adelaide because, even though we lived in New South Wales, our watches were set to South Australian time and we had to catch the South Australian three foot, six inch, northern areas, narrow gauge train, which ran as a tramway, not as a railway, at the designated time from Sulphide Street, not Crystal Street, then go to Cockburn, where they changed locos and renamed it as South Australian Railways, before we went down to Terowie, where we had to change trains again onto the five foot, three inch broad gauge line and when and if we caught the right train, even after all that, we still had a hell of a long way to go before we got to Adelaide.

Got the picture?

The War Hero

I remember when I was about five—it was near the end of the war, like—coming into the kitchen and finding me mum bawling her eyes out. Now, I was wondering what the bloody hell was going on when I saw a letter, written by me dad, sitting there on the table, and I can remember it to this day. It read:

Dear Doris,
I have got the VD and am in Lae hospital and
will be sent home as soon as I am well enough
to travel ...

Well, you could've guessed how I felt. I mean, how many kids do you know who can proudly stand up and say that their dad's got the VD? And I imagined how he got it too: swinging from tree to tree, machine gun blazing, chucking hand grenades and rounding up half the Jap army in an afternoon. And there was me mum, crying with relief that Dad was still alive. So I starts off down the street shouting the good news to all the kids, 'Me dad's got the VD! Me dad's got the VD!'

Well, bugger me dead, if like in a flash Mum wasn't out of that house, grabs me in three strides, and drags me back into the kitchen and, boy, didn't she give me a good dressing-down.

'Now, Swampy, I want you to promise me on the Bible that you won't tell a living soul about yer father gettin' the VD.'

Then Mum tells me that there's spies in the town and if they found out about Dad, they'd kill him when he got home. So I promised not to tell ... and I made the few friends I told promise not to tell either. But I had the feeling that somehow the news spread a bit anyway, because people began dropping around home all concerned about me dad's unfortunate state of health.

Well, soon it was close to the day of me dad's return and, to my amazement, Mum wasn't going to too much trouble over the big event, and the town wasn't preparing anything either. Great thanks, eh, to a man who almost died doing his best for his country! So it was then that I got together with a couple of mates of mine, Brownie and McCaughney, to organise a welcome home fit for a war hero.

When the big day arrived we was good and ready. There was an air of excitement at the railway station, people gathering around to see what a real war hero's VD looked like. Slowly, the old Temora Mail pulls in, grinding to a halt. Weakly, me Dad stepped from the carriage and that's when I gave the signal and down fell our banner:

WELCOME HOME
PRIVATE MARSH ... VD!

Well, things got a bit confusing after that. Dad fainted. Mum broke down again. Some people cheered. Others laughed. The Salvation Army packed up and went home and Aunt Nell, well, she took me to her place ... for a whole month.

Then when I got home, Dad wouldn't tell me how he got the VD. And even to this day I've never seen what it looks like. But that's me dad. Very humble. Unselfish. And he never boasts about his great war feats.

Train Droving

During the 1940s and early 1950s, most of the meatworks used to employ what were called 'train drovers' to look after the sheep or the cattle while they were being transported by rail from the backblocks to the meatworks. I was one of them train drovers and I was paid five shillings per van. There'd be about 120 lambs per sheep wagon, which didn't work out too bad really, especially if you had forty or fifty wagons to look after. And these wagons, they all had little doors at each end so the sheep could be loaded at one end and they'd move right along through, until all the wagons were filled up.

So when the train drover was employed, he got a permit from the railways department to say it didn't cost him to travel. Well, maybe he paid a small fee, but that was refunded when he returned to the station from where he left. Then the train drover slept right down the very end of the train, at the back of the guard's van, in what was called a 'dogbox'. That dogbox contained two little cushion-type bench seats, made from horsehair, and they were about 2 inches thick. That's where you slept. Then there was an access into another small compartment that had a toilet and a washbasin. There were no showers or anything. But if you were lucky, some of the dogboxes had a metal container, about 2 feet long and 6 inches high with some sort of chemical in it so that, when you shook it, it'd heat up and you could put your feet on it to try and keep yourself warm.

And I also remember with the stock trains how the couplings between each wagon had a bit of slack. So when the train moved off there'd be a slight jerk between the first and second wagon, then there'd be a bit bigger jerk between the second and third wagon, and so on and so on. So, if you had fifty wagons, by the time it got right to the end of the train, where you were, there'd be this almighty jerk and you'd just about be thrown off your seat. It certainly threw a few of the sheep off their feet so, at the next stop, your job was to walk along the train and check in each section for the sheep that'd fallen or had been pushed down into a position where they could get smothered and die. Then when you saw a sheep down, you had this long rod with a hook on the end of it, like a staff, and you'd hook that around the sheep and try to pull him over so he could stand up again.

Anyhow, after you'd checked your stock, if time allowed, you'd grab your billy and hop along to the engine driver and he'd fill it from a tap on the steam engine and you could make yourself a cup of tea. Also, some of the larger railway stations had refreshment rooms where you could get sandwiches or whatever, as well as boiling water.

But I was a very quiet sort of bloke, so I didn't get up to too much that'd turn itself into a story. Though, I certainly knew how to make a fool of myself because I remember coming back through Blayney, one time. It was about one o'clock in the morning and, oh, it was a bitterly cold night. Anyway, at Blayney station, as they did at a lot of the bigger railway stations, they had these great big open wood or coal fires to warm the waiting rooms. So I was in there this time, trying to get some feeling back into me bones, when this huge giant of a bloke came in. Oh, he was huge. And he was ugly as well, with this great big coat, and do you know how you get a certain instinct about people? Well, I instantly thought, 'I don't like the look of this bloke. I reckon he's nothing but trouble.'

Anyway, it's always been my way that if you can get someone talking to you then they're less likely to have a go at bashing you up or robbing you. That's my feeling, anyway. So I tried to strike up a conversation with this huge brute of a bloke by saying something stupid like, 'She's a cold night, eh.'

But when I said that, he sort of half turned around and he looked me right in the eye in a very eerie sort of way then he let out a loud grunt at me. And when he grunted it was like you'd imagine the sound that a wild beast makes. Well, I wasn't much taken by that at all. In fact I was a bit shook up over the whole thing, so when the stationmaster came along, I pulled him aside to warn him.

'Look,' I said, 'you'd better keep an eye on that bloke over there. First, I don't like the look of him and, second, he won't talk to anyone and that's a dead giveaway that he's up to no good.'

And the stationmaster said, 'Oh, don't worry about him. That's only Fred. He's deaf and dumb.'

Turk Attack

Now some might reckon that, during the First World War, there was never a shot fired in anger on Australian soil, but there was and it happened right here, just out of Broken Hill. I've pieced together a bit of information from a couple of the old newspapers—*The Conveyor* and the *Barrier Miner*—plus a bit of stuff I've heard around the place, then some other bits that I just added myself.

First, to set the scene: Broken Hill, New Year's Day, 1915. Being a holiday, the Silverton Tramway Company organised two trains to take people out on picnics. One was heading up to McColloch Park, at Stephens Creek, where a Caledonian picnic was being held, the other was going out to Silverton, where the Manchester Unity, Independent Order of Oddfellows had planned its holiday picnic. As this story will tell, one of those picnics was never to happen.

See, there was these two Turkish fellers, Mohammedans they were, one was named Gool Mahomet and the other was Mulla Abdulla. Gool Mahomet was a local ice-cream vendor and Mulla Abdulla was both a camel driver and the Muslim butcher for the Camel Camp, just out of town. Apparently, Mulla Abdulla was a real oddball, with both an odd manner and an odd walk, which was something the local kids teased him about, and that might've also got on his goat and tipped him over the edge.

Anyway, on that fateful morning some of the more keen picnickers were already on the train, waiting for it to be shunted back to the main terminal to pick up the rest of the day-trippers. Now, a few of those picnickers later recalled waving to these two Turks as they drove past on the ice-cream cart, heading in the direction of Silverton, and someone even made the remark how the cart had no chance of getting there until the picnic was well and truly over. But little did they know that, instead of the cart containing ice-cream, it held a stash of guns and ammunition.

So, eventually, the train got going. It was carrying about 1200 men, women and children, travelling in forty open trucks. These trucks usually carted ore but, for this special occasion, they'd been cleaned out and fitted with long wooden seats. Then when the train reached the end of Morgan Street, a few people remembered seeing the ice-cream cart stopped in the distance and by now a red-coloured flag was hanging from its canopy. Of course, nobody took much notice because, in mining terms, a red flag is also a sign that ammunition is being exploded. But as the train got closer, it became evident that the flag was the Turkish one. Again, nobody worried. Even when they could see the two men lying in a nearby pipeline trench with their guns, nobody twigged. For all intents and purposes, they could've been out shooting rabbits.

But then, as the line of railway trucks moved on through a cutting, the Turks opened fire. Now, the newspaper says, and I quote, 'One of the first to fall was Alma Cowries. Her companion Clarrie O'Brien turned to say something … but Alma had already slumped forward, her skull shattered. William Shaw, the foreman of the council's sanitary department, was also fatally wounded and his daughter, Lucy, was hit in the elbow … a third death also occurred at this point. It was Alf Millard, a long-standing employee of the Wood Pipe Company, who was … riding his motorcycle on his usual inspection tour of the pipeline and … he was shot as he passed between the train and the Turks.'

So poor old Alf, eh, talk about being in the wrong place at the wrong time. Anyhow, with all hell breaking loose the train stopped and two men, Paddy Low and Shaw Hendry, took off across to the nearby cemetery caretaker's house to sound the alarm. Of course, when the train driver realised what was going on he planted his foot and moved the train out of the firing line, quick smart.

With the train now gone, the two Turks wandered over to Alf Millard's body, where they had a bit of a chat and decided to head up to Rocky Hill. On their way up, they came across old Dan Jenkins. When old Dan saw that the Turks were carrying guns, he also assumed they were after rabbits and told them, 'You fellers won't get much around here.'

The Turks ignored old Dan and they continued on to the top of Rocky Hill, where old Tom Campbell was standing in the doorway of his one-roomed stone hut.

'You'd better not do any shooting here, there are children around,' Tom warned them. Before he could get in another word the Turks tried to force their way into his hut but Tom slammed the door in their faces. The only trouble was, these Turks then fired through the wooden door and old Tom got hit in the side. He then managed to clamber out the back window and stagger to safety, down to the Allendale Hotel.

The Turks then left old Tom to his own devices and went on past the Camel Camp, where a lot of the Afghans and Indians lived, then headed for a low ridge. But before they got there, they came across a camel owner and driver by the name of Khan Bahader, who just happened to be feeding a goat. He remembered one of the Turks calling out to him, 'Don't follow me or I will shoot you.' Then he fired at Bahader. That one missed but when another bullet flew past Bahader's ear, Bahader yelled, 'If you shoot at me again, I'll get me rifle and shoot you.'

Meanwhile, back in town, word spread like wildfire and everybody had started gathering up their rifles or turning up at the military depot to borrow some to go out after these two Turks. Of course, it was bedlam. In fact, it reads more like a Keystone Kops comedy. The cops started out in two cars but one broke down, so they all piled into the remaining car. Then, rounding the Cable Hotel, they took off across the flat. One of them, a Sergeant Gibson, saw two men in the distance and decided to go over and ask them if they'd seen the Turks. The only trouble was, they turned out to be the two Turks and, as the police car approached the Turks opened fire. The police then screeched to a halt and started to return fire but, being out on the flats, they were an open target and one feller, a Constable Mills, got wounded. Of course, with all this shooting going on it only acted like a magnet and people came from every which way, all eager to get in a shot.

But the killing wasn't over yet. Old Jim Craig was merrily chopping wood in his nearby backyard and, after ignoring his daughter's call to take cover, he was hit by a stray bullet and down he went, dead.

Now I'll read this next bit from the paper because it makes great reading: 'The men of Broken Hill fought on in silent anger. There could be no quarter. As the *Barrier Miner* reported, "There was a desperate determination to leave no work for the hangman or to run the risk of the murderers of peaceful citizens being allowed to escape. The battle ended at 1 pm when the remaining Turk was overwhelmed. Just how it finished is not clear. According to one eyewitness he stood up with something white tied to his rifle and was cut down in the white heat of the town's seething anger. At all events it seems certain the first few hotheads to reach the rocks fired several more rounds through the prone bodies before they could be restrained. Incredibly, one man, Gool Mahomet, was still alive despite his 16 wounds; he died shortly after reaching hospital. The other man, Mulla Abdulla, had apparently died from a head wound received earlier."'

Anyhow, other than the two dead Turks, four innocent people had been killed and seven others were wounded. But all the drama hadn't finished yet. It goes on to say: 'Patriotic fervour blazed strongly and it was argued that the local German community must have been behind the plot. That night restless youths fired the German Club in Delamore Street, and firemen, trying to put out the blaze, found they had to fight the crowd as well as the fire. "Let it burn," was the cry and they tried to cut the fire hoses. Militia with fixed bayonets were called in to keep back the crowd and give the firemen a chance. The club building was gutted but nearby buildings were saved, including an occupied house. It was certainly a wild night in Broken Hill. As the blaze died down, ringleaders marched off to storm the Camel Camp but again their way was barred with cold steel and they saw reason. The militia and police stood guard over the camp all that night. At the top end of Oxide Street the Cable Hotel proudly bore the scars of battle and the Mine Host, Francis Jones, entertained royally.'

So there you go. That's the story of when a couple of Turks attacked the picnic train on its way out to Silverton, during the First World War.

Turkey

Even though this happened back in 1951, I still won't mention names or places as I may incriminate the innocent and the guilty, of which I may or may not have been one of either of those two parties. But tell me if you've heard it before because a few of these things that went on some time ago have been so much spoken about that they've become wide knowledge. Still, this one's based on actual facts even though I might or might not have been there at the time, like I said.

Anyhow, there was this particular train crew that worked out along a small bush branch line and once every week they'd take the old steamer out to deliver and pick up a few goods, plus the occasional passenger, on their way to the end of the line and back. Now, in a pretty isolated spot along this line was situated a turkey farm and throughout the year this train crew had sussed out this mob of turkeys and they were looking delicious.

So by the time they'd started out on their last trip before Christmas they'd decided to swipe one of these turkeys for their Christmas dinner.

Of course, being good mates, the whole crew was in on it, including the guard. So on their way out they pulled up beside this turkey farm. As usual there was no-one about so the fireman hops off with his wheat bag at the ready, he jumps the fence and he grabs one of these turkeys, a nice big plump one. All goes exactly to plan so he jumps back on the train and off they go again with this turkey all wrapped up in the wheat bag, pending Christmas dinner. Now, unbeknown to the train crew, the farmer saw all this happen. So he gets in touch with the cops, explains what he saw, and tells them to meet him at the station at the end of the line. 'Be prepared to make arrests,' the farmer tells the sergeant of police.

Well, just before you get to the station at the end of the line there's this big, walloping, long, sweeping bend. So the train starts to come around this huge bend and the ever-alert fireman sees, in the distance, all these BSA motorbikes lined up on the platform. And the closer they get to the station the more he and the train driver come to realise that these motorbikes belonged to the police.

'What're we gonna do?' said the fireman to the driver. To which the driver took a look at the wheat bag containing the nicked turkey followed by a look towards the firebox. 'Ditch the evidence,' he replied with a tear coming to his eye.

So the fireman grabs the wheat bag and into the firebox it goes. 'Goodbye, Christmas,' he says, and up goes the turkey in a puff of smoke.

Anyhow, when they pull into the station the farmer and the police come aboard and say, 'Alright, where is it?'

'Where's what?' the driver and fireman say.

'The turkey,' the police say.

'We don't know anything about a turkey,' came the reply.

So the police, along with the farmer, search the cab of the train. No turkey there. Then they go digging around in the coal on the tender. No turkey there. So they go through the couple of carriages. Still no turkey. Then they get to the guard's van. 'Have you seen the turkey?' they question the guard.

'What turkey?' he says.

So they scour through the guard's van. Still no turkey.

'Look,' said the driver, 'we're running late and we never run late.' Which was a complete load of bull but with that, the guard blows his whistle and the driver starts moving the train out of the station, leaving the cops to leap back onto the platform, there to try and explain to the farmer how they can't arrest anyone without the evidence being produced.

Anyhow, as it turned out the fireman, who was a pretty clever chap, had brought along an extra wheat bag, just in case. And with knowing that the farmer was still back at the railway station debating the pros and cons of the law with the police, he said to the driver, 'How's about we grab another one on the way back?'

So they did and, yes, I do remember that particular Christmas very well. In fact, it turned out to be one of my most enjoyable Christmases in my many, many years as a fireman on the railways.

Unscratchable

Basically, my story starts with my grandfather. It's a bit hazy, but I know he worked on the construction of the narrow gauge from Peterborough, across the Willochra Plain, to Quorn, in the 1920s, and in about 1936 he worked on the construction of the Port Augusta to Port Pirie line. Then my dad started with the railways in 1936 and ended up as a loco superintendent before retiring in 1978. So between the three of us, we've clocked up well over 100 years with the railways.

But Dad was very well known and he had quite a few 'firsts'. Like, in about 1974, he took the first Indian Pacific to Western Australia. He was also the first to drive the standard gauge Ghan to Marree. He also drove the first Bud Diesel Car out of South Australia. The Bud was a 'passenger' with a similar configuration to the Adelaide metro-trains. He also drove the last steam engine from Port Augusta to Quorn. Unfortunately, he died the October before last but, as a young feller, I used to travel with him on the steam engines to Alice Springs.

That was a remarkable experience because those were very different times and I used to travel on the engine with him, which was absolutely illegal. But one of my favourite memories of being with Dad was on one trip when we were coming back from Alice Springs.

It was around 1954, I'd reckon. Dad was driving the goods down from Alice Springs and we got to a place called Beltana on Christmas Eve. Of course, the crew were all disappointed that they wouldn't be home with their families for Christmas. So, in an attempt to make the most of it, Dad and his fireman went across to the hotel at Beltana to ask the publican, an old chap by the name of Ted Nichols, if he'd put on a bit of a Christmas dinner for us all the next day. Ted was pretty receptive to all that. 'Yep,' he said, 'I'll do that for yer but I'd like a little job done in return.'

Naturally, my father and his fireman said, 'Yeah, that's fine. What do yer want?'

'Oh,' Ted said, 'I need some help to shift a refrigerator.'

In those days the refrigerators were kerosene fridges and they were very, very heavy. Now, poor old Ted had a few physical problems, one of which was he had a glass eye, and another was that he had a wooden leg. Being only very young I wasn't much help, so I was just standing there watching the three of them staggering around with this fridge. But when they got to the doorway they struck trouble because the door wasn't very wide. So, there they were, trying to get this damn fridge through the door when, next thing, poor old Ted's glass eye popped out. Then as he bent over to pick up his eye, his wooden leg fell off. Now, I was absolutely stunned by all this but Dad's fireman, as quick as a flash, said, 'By Jesus, Ted,' he said, 'I've never seen a man fall to pieces so quick under pressure.'

So that's one thing that happened when I was with Dad.

Anyway, when they closed the old Ghan line in 1955, approximately half the railway personnel from Quorn were transferred to Alice Springs and half went to Stirling North, about eight miles from Port Augusta. So in 1959 I started in the Commonwealth Railway's Stores at Stirling North as a 'spud boy'. The job was called a spud boy simply because that's what I did. The spuds would arrive in big hessian bags and I'd put them into smaller bags for retail purposes. I did other things, too, of course. But I was there for about nine months until I passed my entrance exam and joined the railways as an apprentice boilermaker. Then I stayed in the area of the workshops for about ten years before going out on the Nullarbor Plain, doing the fairly unique job of the continuous welding of the railway line. But that's another story.

Now, it might seem like I have some sort of fetish for glass eyes but, while I was in the workshops, this young feller—a real card—well, he had a glass eye. The history there was that his mother had contracted measles when she was pregnant and, as a result, this chap'd been born with only one eye. Then after some years he was fitted with a glass one.

At that stage, I'd just been appointed as an angle-ironsmith. That trade's gone now but, simply, it involved the making or manufacturing of the different forms of steel that weren't produced as a standard by BHP. See, we had steam engines still running around that'd been built back in 1922 and, of course, a lot of the components for those weren't made anymore, so it was my job to make them. The immediate area I worked in had a coke oven and also there was a very big cast-iron block. Now, this block was roughly eight foot square by about two foot thick. It probably weighed six or seven ton and it had a machined flat surface that I could bang away on to form this steel. Anyway, I was standing alongside this block one day and the chap with the glass eye come up, so I said, 'How are yer going?'

'Pretty good,' he said. 'I just got a new eye.'

'Oh,' I said, 'have yer?'

He said, 'Yeah.' And he had this habit of just ripping his glass eye out of its socket to show everybody. So he ripped it out. 'Look,' he said, 'what do yer think of that? It's unscratchable.'

Of course, I said, 'Don't be stupid. Nothing's unscratchable.' I said, 'Look, a diamond's one of the hardest things known to mankind and you can scratch that, so there's no way known that your new glass eye is unscratchable.'

'Bullshit,' he said. 'It's unscratchable.'

With that he got this glass eye of his and he threw it down, hard on the steel block. Well, if you can imagine throwing a golf ball or a marble down onto a steel block, well, this eye simply rebounded off the block and it shot straight up in the air. Now, like many workshops of the day, the roof was angled like the teeth of a saw. At its highest it was 59 feet. Anyway, up goes this eye and, of course, he's running around with his hands held out, ready to catch it when it comes down. But it doesn't come down, see.

'I've lost me eye,' this feller said.

'I'll get it,' I said. And so I went to the 60 ton overhead crane driver and I asked him if he'd drive me up and down the workshop on his crane to see if I could find this glass eye, up in the roof.

'Okay,' he said.

So this driver took me along until, sure enough, in one of the gables up in the rafters here's this eye looking at me. It was a bit hairy but I climbed up the edge of the crane and onto the rafters and picked the eye up out of all the dust and crap. Then I took the eye back down and gave it back to the bloke who'd lost it.

'Thanks,' he said, and without even wiping it, he just stuck it straight back in his eye socket. But then he must've thought about it because he popped it back out again and he showed me.

'See, have a look,' he said. 'I told you it was unscratchable.'

And so help me God, there wasn't a mark on it.

What's Up, Doc?

When I first joined the railways in Tasmania, things still worked pretty much as they'd done for near on the past 100 years. It was still mostly steam, it was the same system, the same type of people, the same operations were still running. You name it, nothing much had changed. So struth, you look back on those days, perhaps not with love but certainly with a kind of fondness.

And mostly they were good times and a lot of hilarious things used to happen, like the old story of stopping and picking mushrooms. I mean, we did that lots of times when we were out on goods trains. If ever you saw a patch of mushrooms out in the paddock, it was, 'Oh, all of a sudden we've got a terrible brake problem.' So the brake'd come on or the brake box'd fall off—any excuse—and you'd go and fill your hat or whatever with the mushrooms. Then you'd fire back on engine and off you'd go again because, invariably, you'd be stopping the night at some country barracks or other and you'd cook up those mushrooms for tea.

But those sorts of things happened all the time. I can remember being told a story. I guess it would've been in the 1940s. Anyway, there was a depot at the end of the Derwent Valley line called Fitzgerald. Fitzgerald's a little scattered town out in the middle of Woop Woop. The main road was only a bush track up on the hill, a couple of miles above the railway station. It's in rainforest country so it's mainly timber industry. But, oh, it was a wild and woolly place.

Now, most of the railway chaps were single men and they lived there in a barracks, which was stuck in the middle of a 'Y'. In Tasmania, a 'Y' is the track where you turn engines. It's called a 'triangle' in other states of Australia. Oh, there's lots of funny things in Tasmania that I can tell you about, like someone calling someone a 'rumone'. That's short for 'rum one'. It's a Tasmanianism you won't hear anywhere else in Australia and it means you're an 'odd bod'.

Anyway, this barracks at Fitzgerald was very small. They only had enough room for four or five single men's bedrooms with a combined kitchen–dining area that had a fuel stove. And of course, being single, all these fellows drank lots and lots and lots of beer, to such an extent that supplies would run out on a frighteningly regular basis. Now, you've got to remember that roads around that neck of the woods were virtually nonexistent, so there were very few cars around. But the nearest pub was at National Park, which is the famous Mount Field National Park, where we ran trains on a regular basis.

So on a Sunday the crews would have one of the locos steaming away in the engine shed, all banked up, ready to run. Then when they run out of grog, they'd all hop aboard and away they'd go. Oh, there'd be about eight or nine of them all squeezed in the cabin, so there'd be a bit of a crowd. Anyhow, they'd tear off down the track, hoping that nothing else was on the line, and they'd head for National Park.

Now, just past National Park, away from the road, there was a cutting and that's where they'd hide the engine. They'd just bank it up, put the handbrake on and off to the pub they'd go. Then after they'd had their fill, just in case of an emergency, they'd buy a barrel of beer, roll it down the track, load it onto the engine, then they'd go at breakneck speed back to Fitzgerald which, as you might imagine, would've been a hairy-scary trip.

But near where they used to park the loco there was a house, and I don't remember the lady's name but she'd see all these goings-on and she'd inform the railway office in Hobart how these fellows were up to no good. But, of course, in those days, the grapevine was extremely efficient so each time some official or other came sneaking around, these fellows would be acting like angels. Anyhow, because they knew this lady was dobbing them in, whenever they saw her standing on the platform, waiting to catch the train, they'd just give her a wave and shoot straight past.

Then there was another train driver called Doc. Doc lived in a camp down behind the barracks that we'd named 'Skid Row', so you can just imagine what it was like. Anyway, Doc kept a cow near the barracks so that whenever the crews wanted milk they'd just go out and milk this cow. Now Doc looked after this old cow like it was a pet, you know, so it was always hanging around the barracks. Then, of course, they had a vegetable garden there, which was another of Doc's pet projects. Having a vegetable garden was very common with railway blokes. They had gardens all over the place. It's known Australia-wide that railwaymen were good gardeners. Anyway, these blokes were on the booze one night, as per usual, and, at one stage, one of the train drivers, old Rastus, he staggered back into the common room and yelled, 'Somethin's out there's eatin' the f'n lettuces.'

And old Doc, who was in his usual drunken state, replied, 'Don't worry, Rastus. I'll sort it out.'

So Doc grabbed his shotgun and he stumbled outside. Next thing they hear is this almighty *Boom!* And you can just imagine it: Doc, coming back into the barracks and standing at the door, with his big hat stuck back on his head, the barrel of his shotgun still smoking. Then he looked around the room for a bit, wide-mouthed, with a bewildered look in his eye.

'What's up, Doc?' the fellers asked.

'I'll be stuffed,' Doc slurred. 'I think I just shot me own bloody cow.'

Where's the Barra?

My name's Brian Gibbs and between 1956 and 1961 I was the officer-in-charge of the Normanton to Croydon Railway, in the north-west of Queensland. That particular piece of track is reputed to be the most remote and isolated rail line in Australia. Anyhow, I drove the petrol-driven rail motor, more commonly known as a Tin Hair, on its weekly trip from Normanton to Croydon and return, and I'd like to share a couple of short memories of my time with that grand old rail motor, officially named the 'Gulflander'.

Back in 1956 we had a huge cyclone in the Gulf of Carpentaria, the results of which caused widespread damage and many rivers to flood. From memory, two people lost their lives in Georgetown. That's how bad it was. Anyhow, as the cyclone continued its journey over towards Cairns we were still keen to do our weekly trip, which we did, and the rail motor made it to Croydon okay.

But when we started back to Normanton on the Thursday morning, we only got 20 miles and we found that the Seventy-Four Mile Creek bridge was covered with floodwater. She was well over the top. Anyhow, I decided that we should still have a go at crossing the bridge, but then the flywheel became covered with water and it consequently splashed water all over the engine. That was no good, so we were forced to reverse the Gulflander all the way back to Croydon. The best we could do on the return was 5 miles an hour, which made it a very long journey.

The following morning, the Friday, we detached two wagons and we set out once again for Normanton, hoping now that the creek was crossable. But when we came to the Seventy-Four Mile Creek, the level of the water was much the same. So this time we shut the motor off and decided that our best option was to push the vehicle through the water, over the bridge, which proved to be a considerable distance. After much effort we made it, though I felt that we were lucky because the railway line was flat and did not dip, as it did at other points along the way. Mind you, in saying that, as we continued the journey we were forced to get out and push the rail motor at three more locations.

When we eventually reached the Norman River, the water was a good four to six inches above the rails and, with a little care plus a good slice of luck, we were just able to cross the river and head towards our destination of Normanton. And we made it, but due to the severe flooding that soon followed we were unable to continue the rail motor service to Croydon for the next ten weeks.

So that's one memory. Another one's how the patrons in at the pub in Croydon often used to complain that they'd never seen any of the barramundi—or barra, as we call it—I'd apparently skited so much about catching in the Norman River, at Normanton.

'Okay then,' I said, 'I'll prove it to you.'

'Yeah,' they replied. 'When?'

'Next trip,' I said.

With that settled, the following Tuesday afternoon, John Hindmarsh, the then Powerhouse Superintendent, and myself went fishing at Glenore, about 12 miles south-east of Normanton. I was very confident of a good catch there because I knew a nice little spot beside the rail bridge, over the Norman River.

Anyhow, we fished out of a rowing boat, trailing a lure, and before long we'd caught two nice sized barra, one about 15 pounds, the other around 18 pounds. Seeing how my next trip to Croydon was just the following morning, I decided that I'd really give the blokes at the pub a treat and I'd deliver these two fish to them nice and fresh. With that in mind, John and I proceeded to tie a line to the mouth of each of the fish. We then placed them in a large waterhole, in the river, under the bridge. Finally, we tied the other end of the lines to a tree, then we left the barra there to swim and stay alive. The next morning it was just a simple matter of stopping the rail motor on the bridge, going down, collecting the fish and taking them to Croydon where I'd prove to all my doubters, once and for all, just what a great fisherman I was.

So on the Wednesday morning I stopped the Gulflander on the bridge and hurried down to the waterhole. I pulled on one of the lines, but no fish. The line was broken. I had a look around and I saw the barra up on dry land, about 4 yards away. 'This's funny,' I thought. 'The only way it could've got up that far was if it'd been thrown or it'd somehow jumped out of the waterhole.'

When I tried the other line it seemed to be snagged, so I gave it a good pull. But no, it was stuck firm. By this stage the passengers in the rail motor were looking expectantly down at me so I thought, 'Geez, I'd better not disappoint them.'

So I removed one shoe and the sock and I stuck my foot in the waterhole and manoeuvred it around in an attempt to clear the snag. No, that didn't work. It was hooked on something solid; something that felt very much like a rough log. 'Blow it,' I thought, so I grabbed the line again and gave it one hell of a yank and up shot the head of a crocodile, jaws open and ready for a fight.

Well, bugger the fish—they could say what they darn well liked in at the Croydon pub. I was out of there in a shot, much to the amusement of my rail passengers.

Whodunit?

History will tell you that General MacArthur uttered his famous words 'I shall return' while he was standing on Terowie railway station. That was in about March 1942, after he'd escaped the Philippines because the Japs had invaded the place.

So that was one piece of history that happened on Terowie railway station, and a lot of people might already know that. But I reckon not too many would know that on the very same railway platform, back on 22 March 1921, the first political assassination in this country, arguably, took place. Now I say arguably because while history may state that it was, a) a political assassination and, b) it was carried out by a 'mad Russian', I differ on both those points.

A bit of background. Terowie was the juncture of two important rail lines. First was the Alice Springs to Adelaide line, which was the line General MacArthur was on, and second, it's where you change to the narrow gauge trains to go to Broken Hill. And that's just what

Percy Brookfield, the state Labor parliamentarian for Broken Hill, was doing when he got shot.

Now, the newspapers of the day built their assassination theory around someone having a political gripe against Percy. See, Percy held the balance of power in the Labor-run state government of New South Wales and he was also the driving force behind the agreement for the unions on the eight-hour day. Anyhow, things weren't going his way so he gave his own colleagues the ultimatum, 'If you don't give us the eight-hour day then I'll cross the floor and the opposition will be in government.'

Now, for any politician to go against his own party was a brave thing to do and he made some pretty strong enemies over that. But that didn't worry Percy. He was all for the people of Broken Hill and he always fought for improved conditions for the workers, the miners in particular.

Then at Terowie on 22 March 1921, when he was so-called assassinated, his enemies leaked it to the newspapers how Percy had been shot in the back while trying to run away from a 'mad Russian'. But that was all wrong, because the bigger wound was found to be in his back, not his front, making it obvious that the bullet went in his chest and out his back, not the other way around. Now, it's my feeling that the newspapers only spun that story to make Percy look like he was a coward, a chicken, because they didn't want a leftish or communist type to get any fame.

The next thing I'd challenge was Percy Brookfield's death being at the hands of a 'mad Russian'. I say that because both my grandmother and my aunty told me that Percy was having an affair with another bloke's wife, up here in Broken Hill, and this bloke, who wasn't even Russian, said, 'Right, I'm gonna meet that bastard down at Terowie and sort him out good and proper.'

So there you go. Was it a political assassination or not, and whodunit, a mad Russian or was it some jealous, irate, mad husband? Of course, history doesn't mention any of this and, anyway, it was easier to name the killer as being a mad Russian because Russians weren't that popular back then.

But, oh, Percy Brookfield, he was certainly very popular up here. His funeral was the biggest Broken Hill's ever seen, either before or since. The procession went for miles and Percy's was the biggest candle grave in the local cemetery. That shows you just how highly respected he was. But my grandmother believed, as did my aunty, that no matter what good Percy Brookfield did for the workers, the moment he had it off with another man's wife, that was it as far as they were concerned. So they were about the only people in town who refused to go to the funeral.

So there you go. I'll leave it with you. History isn't always as it's written, eh? Oh, it might've been right in the case of General MacArthur, but was it right in the case of Percy Brookfield? I tend to agree with my grandmother and my aunty because they just about knew everything that went on in Broken Hill ... sometimes even before it happened.

'X' Marks the Spot

You know that song 'I've Been Everywhere'? Well, over my time with the New South Wales Railways, I just about went everywhere. Soon after I joined I was sent up to Tamworth, as a booking officer—booking seats for people, checking things, balancing things and doing a summary of the station's everyday work. Then I went on relief. See, while people went on holidays or whatever, that's when I got shoved out to all different towns. Oh, I floated all up through the north-west to places like Moree, Inverell, Narrabri, Karangi, Tamworth, Werris Creek, Murrurundi and that.

But, in that sort of job, most of your life's spent in the suitcase, travelling from one town to another, staying in pubs. See, when I was away they'd cover for my accommodation and things like that, but when I got back to my home station at Tamworth, they didn't cover for anything. I mean, at one stage, while I was back in Tamworth, I was paying more in hotel accommodation than what I was earning in wages. 'This's not much bloody use,' I thought, so I ended up staying in a private house.

Anyway, after that I went back to Sydney for a while before going down to Junee, again on relief. And, I suppose, I spent about five or six years down there, and I did all that area out the south-west—Griffith, Leeton, Narrandera, Hay, Albury, Wagga and all that.

But Junee was an interesting place. It was a big junction for all the trains, and we certainly had some times. I struck one job there called the Back Shift Roster Clerk. My hours were from eleven o'clock at night through till quarter past eight in the morning, and when you did the roster for the train crews, well, a lot of them had to be transferred onto the trains that were going back to where they'd come from. That's why it was called the 'back shift'. So these blokes, they'd be locals or they were staying in pubs or boarding houses or down the railway barracks. Then, before their train was due to leave, you sent out a call boy on his bicycle to wake them up so they could get ready in time to get down to their allotted train. Now, it was up to each member of the train's crew to let the back shift roster clerk know the time they wanted to be woken up. Like, some of them wanted to be called an hour before their train left, others two hours; whatever they stipulated.

Now, some of those blokes were pretty prickly characters, I can tell you. There was one guard, he was a local—Ken Nuttle was his name, though it mightn't do to mention that. He did shiftwork like I did. I used to stay at the Hotel Junee and I used to drink with him quite a bit. Anyhow, Ken was married and he lived in a house near the pub, in the same street that ran along the railway line. So he lived pretty close by. Ken always wanted to be called exactly one hour before his train departed. But on this particular night, I completely forgot and by the time I remembered and got the call boy to ride down to Ken's place to wake him up, he hardly had any time at all to get himself ready.

So it's two o'clock in the morning and I'm sitting there in the office and the next thing I hear is Ken singing out from his house, 'Parry, you f'n bastard. Yer didn't give me a one hour call. I shouldn't be comin' ta work, yer bloody f'n mongrel.'

Oh, he really went off his beam, you know, giving me this big stir. And on and on he went, getting stuck into me. And at that time of the morning, because the air's so still, all this abuse just echoed around the town. Then, a week later, in the local Junee rag some enterprising reporter wrote, 'All of Junee was woken on such-and-such a night when the back shift roster clerk failed in his duties to wake a particular guard at the appropriate time.'

But anyway, it all worked out okay. That time, Ken only went on a short run—he did his eight hours, like—but when he came back that afternoon I was in the pub and he come over and he said, 'Ah, I'd better buy yer a bloody beer. I guess yer not a bad sort'a bloke.'

So, yes, some of the members of those train crews were very touchy characters. In fact Stan Conroy, a mate of mine, he also rostered the train crews and he had a book and in that book he had the list of their names and beside each he'd either have three X's, two X's, one X or a star, and he'd never tell anyone what it all meant. But he told me. He said, 'Norm,' he said, 'it's me grading system for these crews.' He said, 'The star's fer a bloke who's not a bastard, one X is fer a sort of a bastard, two X's is fer not so bad a bastard and three X's is fer a fair-dinkum downright bastard of a bastard of a bastard's bastard.'

A Railway Reverie

Okay, I'll just finish up with a poem. This comes from the *Railway Institute Magazine*, years and years ago. I don't know who wrote it, but do you know what a roundhouse is? A roundhouse is like a garage for the locomotives. If you can imagine a huge circular shed with an open centre and in the middle of it there's a turntable, right? Then fanning out from this turntable are lots of tracks going off into the various 'garages'. So, a locomotive comes in from outside the roundhouse and onto this turntable. The turntable then goes around until the loco was pointed into whatever 'garage' it's going in, right? That's how the roundhouse worked, and these days there's still a lot of them around. The only trouble is that a lot of the old steam locos have just been left sitting in them. It's sad really, but anyway, here's the poem titled 'A Railway Reverie':

I wandered through the depot
On a cold and dreary morn
When I saw an old-time steamer
All silent and forlorn.
The windows cracked and broken
And a bird's nest in her stack
Made memories start a'flooding
And the years went rolling back.

I saw my old big wheeler
Which hauled the Crack Express
(for better class of loco
one could never wish).
She could run the tightest schedule
And was never known to pack
When I opened up her throttle
and notched the lever back.

Here stood a mighty freighter
That climbed the mountainside
You could hear her beat in frosty air
For many railway miles.
With overload and underload
She was monarch of the track
Yet, she did not stem the sadness
Of the thoughts that flooded back.

I saw the dirty tanker
That shunted in the yard
And made my heavy consist up
With take-out's small and hard.
She snatched at vans and wagons
Steaming there and back
She also had a place among
The thoughts that flooded back.

Then I saw the gleaming diesels
With their polish and their chrome
To sit inside their pretty cab
I would not feel at home.
There'd be no rain upon my face
No wind to tug my cap
To me they have no memories
That keep a'coming back.

'Cause I'm just an old-time driver
With nothing much to do
Just mooching through a roundhouse
To kill an hour or two.
And the more I see, I realise
There's something here I lack
It's those mates I knew in years gone by
Whose memories call me back.